W9-AMM-218

To...

From..

Illustrated by Caroline Jayne Church and Stuart Trotter
Cover illustrations by Christine Tappin
Original prayers written by Meryl Doney and Jan Payne
Designed by Chris Fraser at Page to Page

This edition published by Parragon Books Ltd in 2014 and distributed by

Parragon Inc.
440 Park Avenue South, 13th Floor
New York, NY 10016
www.parragon.com

ISBN 978-1-4723-6790-7

Printed in China

A Prayer a Day

365 Prayers for Children

Bath • New York • Cologne • Melbourne • Delhi
Hong Kong • Shenzhen • Singapore • Amsterdam

Contents

Wonderful World
6–59

Animal Blessings
60–111

Giving Thanks
112–155

My Family
156–203

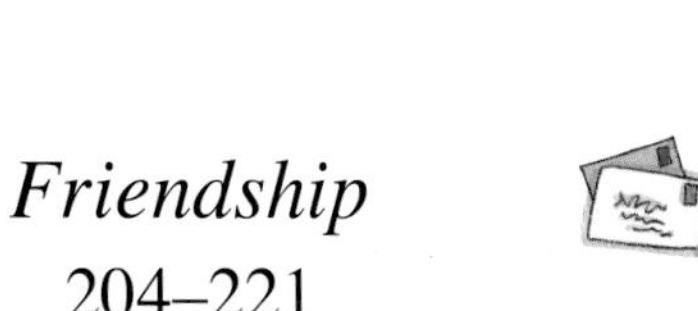

Friendship
204–221

Following God
222–265

Good Morning
266–293

Special Days
294–335

Time for Bed
336–375

Index Of First Lines
376–383

Wonderful World

All things bright and beautiful,
All creatures, great and small,
All things wise and wonderful,
The Lord God made them all.

Each little flower that opens,
Each little bird that sings,
He made their glowing colors,
He made their tiny wings.

The tall trees in the greenwood,
The meadows where we play,
The rushes by the water
We gather every day.

He gave us eyes to see them,
And lips that we might tell
How great is God almighty,
Who has made all things well.

Cecil Francis Alexander (1823–1895)

Thank you, God, for showing me
The perfect beauty of a tree.
I didn't know a tree could be
Remarkable, like you and me.

God made the world so broad and grand,
Filled with blessings from his hand.
He made the sky so high and blue,
And all the little children, too.

Anonymous

For every bright green leaf unfurled,
Thank you, God—what a wonderful world!

In the beginning, God looked at everything that he had made and he saw that it was very good. When I look at the world I say, "Thank you, God, for making it very, very good."

Dear God, bless our nets as we cast and trawl;
The ocean is deep and our ship is small.

Traditional

For this new morning and its light,
For rest and shelter of the night,
For health and food, for love and friends,
For every gift your goodness sends,
We thank you, gracious Lord.

Anonymous

Bright is the morning,
New is the day;
When I wake,
To God I say—
"Good morning!"

Cool is the evening,
At close of day;
Before I sleep,
To God I say—
"Good night!"

Dear God,
I like grass.
It grows and grows.
It tickles me
Between my toes.
It's like a carpet
Spread for me.
And it's as green
As green can be.

For flowers that bloom about our feet,
Father we thank thee.
For tender grass so fresh, so sweet,
Father we thank thee.
For the bird and hum of bee,
For all things fair we hear or see,
Father in heaven, we thank thee.

Ralph Waldo Emerson (1803–1882)

When astronauts look back at our world from the moon, they see that it is beautiful—blue and green and white with clouds. Help us keep our world clean and beautiful because it's such a special place.

For a million stars that sparkle
In a sky of darkest blue—
I cannot count the stars,
But, God, I can thank you.

For air and sunshine, pure and sweet,
We thank our heavenly Father;
For grass that grows beneath our feet,
We thank our heavenly Father;
For lovely flowers the hedge along,
For graceful trees with branches strong,
For birds that sing their joyful song,
We thank our heavenly Father.

Anonymous

The green land stretches to the sea
and we who live on it can travel
and enjoy the lanes and hills,
the sheep and goats and cows,
the streams and rocks, the beaches
and the sand. We thank you, God,
for this good land.

Tomorrow is a special day
I'm off on vacation—hooray!
I'm going where there's sand and sea,
And lots of treats for you and me.
Where ponies give rides on the beach,
And seagulls fly just out of reach.

Dear God,
Thank you for the sun so bright
That fills the world with dazzling light.
And thank you for the muffled sound
When snow lies thickly on the ground.

A special thanks for gentle rain,
Which helps the grass grow green again.
But please, God, send the wind, I pray
So I can fly my kite today.

The year's at the spring;
the day's at the morn;
morning's at seven;
the hill-side's dew-pearled;
the lark's on the wing;
the snail's on the thorn;
God's in his heaven—
all's right with the world!

Robert Browning (1812–1889)

Dear God,
I know it's spring
When I hear the birds sing.
They're thanking you
For making things new.

Summer suns are glowing
Over land and sea,
Happy light is flowing
Bountiful and free.
Everything rejoices
In the mellow rays,
All earth's thousand voices
Swell the psalm of praise.

Bishop How (1823–1897)

I love to see the raindrops
Splashing on the sidewalks;
I love to see the sunlight
Twinkling in the rain;
I love to see the wind-gusts
Drying up the raindrops;
I love to feel the sunshine
Coming out again.

Thank you for the thunderstorm,
Thank you for the wind and rain,
And thank you for the sunshine
Coming out again.

When it rains in summer,
When the sky turns gray,
When the rain clouds gather
And I can't go out to play,
Then I see the wet grass
And it makes me think,
How glad I am that all the plants
Have lovely rain to drink!

Roses are red,
Violets are blue.
When it rains, dear God,
I thank you!

Plants need the water
Just as we do.
For sending the rain, dear God,
We thank you!

Thank you for the special time
When winds begin to blow
And golden leaves come tumbling down
Setting the earth aglow.

I know the summer's over now,
And winter's on its way,
But I am full of happiness
On this colorful, bright day.

Oh, thought I!
What a beautiful thing
God has made winter to be,
By stripping trees
And letting us see
Their shape and forms.
What a freedom does it seem
To give them to the storms.

Dorothy Wordsworth (1771–1855)

God bless the field and bless the furrow,
Stream and branch and rabbit burrow.
Bless the minnow, bless the whale,
Bless the rainbow and the hail.
Bless the nest and bless the leaf,
Bless the righteous and the thief.
Bless the wing and bless the fin,
Bless the air I travel in.
Bless the mill and bless the mouse,
Bless the miller's bricken house.
Bless the earth and bless the sea,
God bless you and God bless me.

Anonymous

Dear God,
The end of summer is sad—
But you give us apples
To make us glad!

I peeked through the curtain
When I woke in the night.
Great, gray flakes
Were an amazing sight.

I woke in the morning,
And to my delight,
All the world was
Sparkling white!

Snowdrops,
Ice drops,
Raindrops
Fall.
Sun shines down
To kiss them all.
See them sparkle in the light,
Winter's wonders
Jewel-bright.
Snowdrops,
Ice drops,
Raindrops
All,
Show God's love
For great and small.

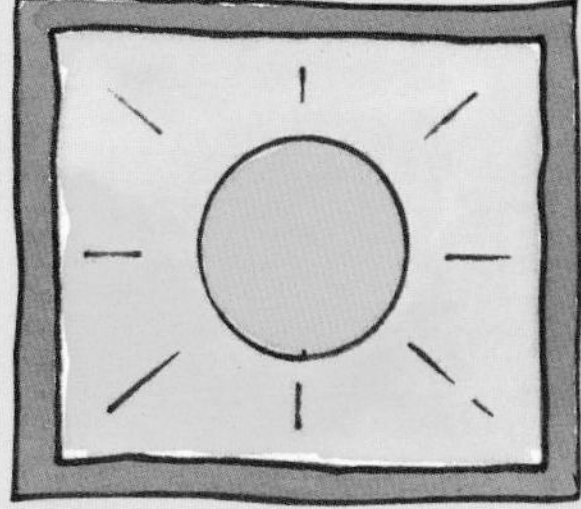

In winter, all the creatures
Shelter from the storm.
Thank you, God, for homes that keep us
Safe and warm.

Oh God! who giv'st the winter's cold,
As well as summer's joyous rays,
Us warmly in thy love enfold,
And keep us through life's wintry days.

S. Longfellow (1819–1892)

In the middle of winter
At dead of night,
That's when God was born on earth,
King of light.

Joy to the world!
The Lord is come;
Let earth receive her King;
Let every heart
Prepare him room,
And heav'n and nature sing,
And heav'n and nature sing,
And heav'n, and heav'n
And nature sing.

Joy to the world!
The Savior reigns;
Let men their songs employ,
While fields and floods,
Rocks, hills and plains
Repeat the sounding joy,
Repeat the sounding joy,
Repeat, repeat
The sounding joy.

Isaac Watts (1674–1748)

Praise the Lord! Ye heavens adore him,
Praise him, angels in the height!
Sun and moon, rejoice before him,
Praise him, all ye stars and light.

John Kempthorne (1775–1838)

We can praise God on the trumpet,
We can praise him on the drum,
We can praise him with our dancing,
We can whistle, shout or hum.
We can praise God on the violin
Or use our voice to sing,
We can make a very joyful noise
On almost anything!

Lord thy glory fills the heaven,
Earth is with its fullness stored;
Unto thee be glory given,
Holy, holy, holy Lord.

Bishop Mant (1776–1848)

Praise the Lord! Praise him on earth, praise him in heaven. Praise him for the wonderful things he has done, and just for being God.

From Psalm 150

All things praise thee, Lord most high!
Heaven and earth and sea and sky!
Time and space are praising thee!
All things praise thee; Lord, may we!

George William Conder (1821–1874)

I may be small,
But I can sing
A song of praise
To God the king.

Praise the Lord from the heavens,
praise him in the heights!
Praise him, all his angels,
praise him, all his host!

Praise him, sun and moon,
praise him, all you shining stars!
Praise him, you highest heavens,
and you waters above the heavens!

Praise the Lord from the earth,
you sea monsters and all deeps,
fire and hail, snow and frost,
stormy wind fulfilling his command!

Mountains and all hills,
fruit trees and all cedars!
Wild animals and all cattle,
creeping things and flying birds!

Kings of the earth and all peoples,
princes and all rulers of the earth!
Young men and women alike,
old and young together!

Let them praise the name of the Lord,
for his name alone is great.

From Psalm 148

Dear God, I love to be on the beach
where the sand meets the ocean.
It reminds me what a wonderful world you've made.

On the beach I can look far out
where the ocean meets the sky,
and know that there's a wonderful world out there.

Perhaps one day
I'll go traveling and see the world.

Thank you for flowers,
Thank you for trees,
Thank you for grasses
That toss in the breeze.
Thank you for vegetables,
Thank you for spice,
Thank you for everything
That makes food taste nice.
Thank you, dear Father,
For all things that grow
In sunshine and rain,
And the glowing rainbow.

Glory be to God for dappled things.

G. M. Hopkins (1844–1889)

Two eyes to see, two ears to hear,
one nose to smell, one mouth to tell.
How great is God who gave them to me.

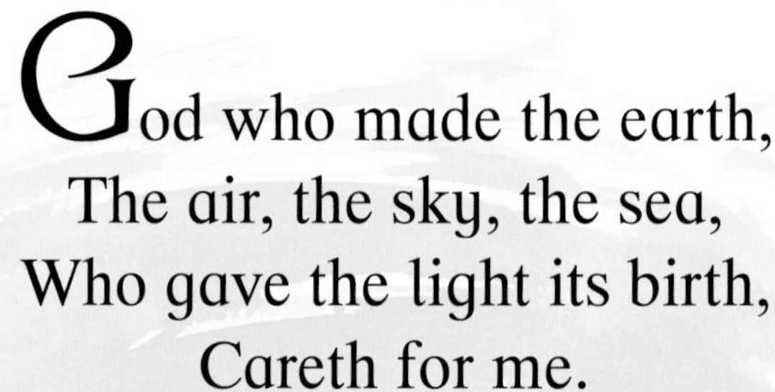

God who made the earth,
The air, the sky, the sea,
Who gave the light its birth,
Careth for me.

Sarah Betts Rhodes (1824–1904)

Wide as the world,
(spread arms wide)

Deep as the sea,
(point down deep)

High as the sky,
(point up high)

Is your love for me.
(hug yourself)

Dear God, thank you for our town;
for all the beautiful and surprising things
we can see in the streets and gardens,
for sparkles in the sidewalk, rainbows
in the puddles, blossom petals fluttering
in the gutter, and sun glinting off the
windowpanes. They make walking
down the road an exciting journey.

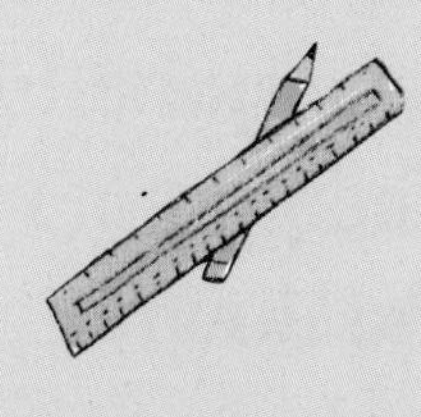

School is over.
We fold our hands, and thank
the Lord, who has been with us.

Ms Margot Damjakob (1939–1940)

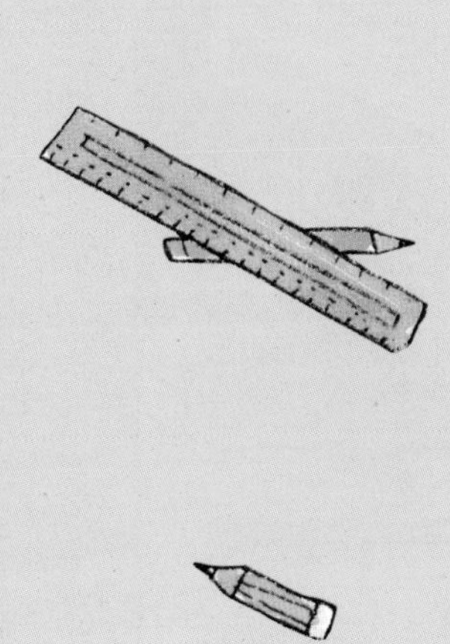

Lord, make me see your glory
in every place.

Michelangelo (1475–1564)

When I travel in a bus I see the streets and houses. When I go in a train, I see the fields and hills. When I fly in an airplane, I can see the whole country.

If I could go up in a rocket, I would see the whole world. Thank you, God, for travel. It shows me what a great world you have made.

Animal Blessings

Jesus our brother, strong and good,
Was humbly laid in a manger of wood,
And the friendly beasts around him stood,
Jesus our brother, strong and good.

"I," said the donkey, shaggy and brown,
"I carried his mother uphill and down,
I carried her safely to Bethlehem town;
I," said the donkey, shaggy and brown.

"I," said the cow, all white and red,
"I gave him my manger for his bed,
I gave him my hay to pillow his head,
I," said the cow, all white and red.

"I," said the sheep with the curly horn,
"I gave him my wool for his blanket warm,
He wore my coat on Christmas morn;
I," said the sheep with the curly horn.

"I," said the dove, from the rafters high,
"Cooed him to sleep, my mate and I;
We cooed him to sleep, my mate and I;
I," said the dove, from the rafters high.

And every beast by some good spell,
In the stable dark was glad to tell,
Of the gift he gave Immanuel,
The gift he gave Immanuel.

Traditional carol (c. 1300)

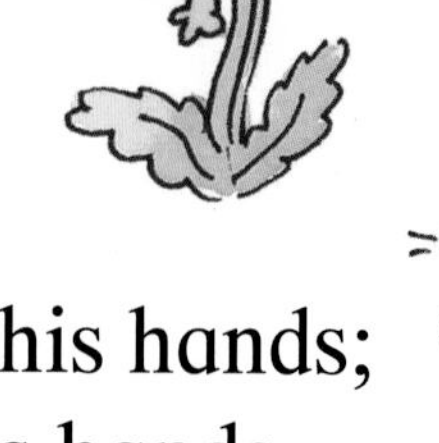

He's got the whole world in his hands;
He's got the whole world in his hands.

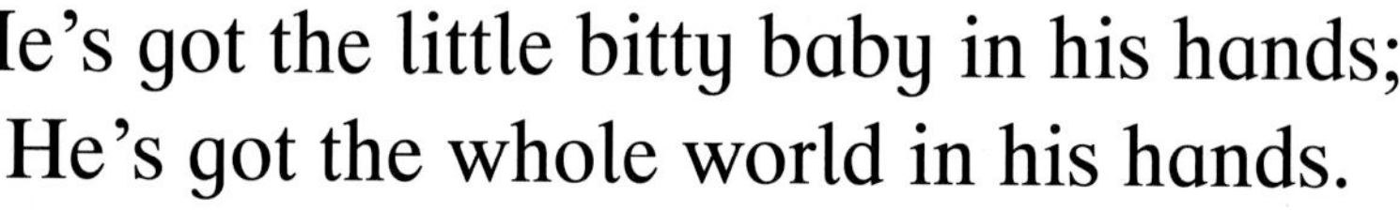

He's got the little bitty baby in his hands;
He's got the whole world in his hands.

He's got the trees and flowers in his hands;
He's got the whole world in his hands.

He's got the wind and the rain in his hands;
He's got the whole world in his hands.

He's got the seas and the rivers in his hands;
He's got the whole world in his hands.

He's got you and me, brother, in his hands;
He's got you and me, sister, in his hands.

He's got the whole world in his hands!

Traditional spiritual

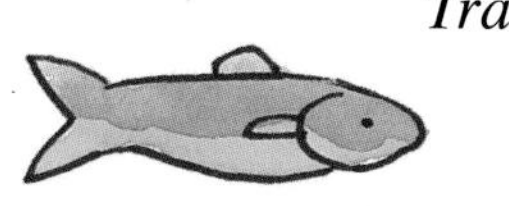

Thank you, God, that the world is wide;
that there are so many countries and
so many different people.

Thank you, God, that the seas are deep;
that the oceans are full of amazing creatures,
which swim and dive and play.

Thank you, God, that the sky is high;
that the stars we see twinkling in the night
are moving in the vast areas of space.

Thank you, God, that I'm in this wide, deep, high
world with you.

Thank you, God, for giving us
The hippo and rhinoceros.
For crazy monkeys, brash and loud,
Giraffes with heads stuck in the cloud.
Thanks for parrots bold and bright,
And zebras smart in black and white.

For elephants with giant feet,
And anteaters so trim and neat.
I wouldn't want the world to be
Empty except for you and me.

Dear God, I had some yummy honey for lunch. Then I saw a show on TV about how bees make honey, and talk to each other, and make their hive ready for winter. I was amazed at how they do it all and how busy they are. Now when I have honey I say, “Thank you bees for making honey— and thank you God for making bees.”

Dear God, I heard
The song of a bird,
Singing for joy in the morning.
It made my heart sing
Like anything
That I am alive, like him.

The little cares that fretted me,
I lost them yesterday.
Among the fields, above the sea,
Among the winds at play,
Among the lowing herds,
The rustling of the trees,
Among the singing of the birds,
The humming of the bees.

The foolish fears of what might pass,
I cast them away,
Among the clover-scented grass,
Among the new-mown hay,
Among the hushing of the corn
Where the drowsy poppies nod,
Where ill thoughts die and good are born—
Out in the fields with God.

Louise Imogen Guiney (1861–1920)

Little lamb, who made thee?
Dost thou know who made thee?
Gave thee life and bade thee feed
By the stream and over the mead;
Gave thee clothing of delight,
Softest clothing, woolly, bright;
Gave thee such a tender voice
Making all the vales rejoice?
Little lamb, who made thee?
Dost thou know who made thee?

William Blake (1757–1827)

I thank God for my rabbit,
Who's soft and furry
And wiggles his nose
All the time—it's his habit.

The song of the wren,
The smallest bird,
Is the biggest and strongest
I've ever heard.
He's praising God
For his little nest,
And I think he'll burst
With happiness!

Lo, the winter is past, the rain is over and gone, the flowers appear on the earth, the time of the singing of the birds is come, and the voice of the turtle dove is heard in the land.

From The Song of Solomon

From ghoulies and ghosties,
long-leggety beasties, and things
that go bump in the night,
good Lord deliver us.

Traditional

He prayeth best, who loveth best
All things both great and small;
For the dear God who loveth us,
He made and loveth all.

Samuel Taylor Coleridge (1772–1834)

The worm is
very plain,
but then again
the worm is
very good
at what he does.
Without him
my garden
would not live.
So thank you, God,
for worms
And all they give.

Beetles are funny,
Ants are too,
Flies have fantastic wings.
Sometimes I like them
So my prayer is,
"Thank you, God, for the smallest things."

Spiders are scary,
Mice are too,
Moths have fluttery wings.
Sometimes I hate them
So I say, "Help me
Not to be scared of the smallest things!"

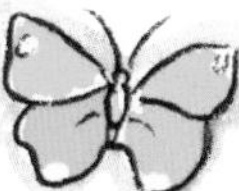

No shop does the bird use,
No counter nor baker,
But the bush is his orchard,
The grass is his acre.
The ant is his quarry,
The seed is his bread,
And a star is his candle
To light him to bed.

Elizabeth Coatsworth (1893–1986)

When dogs bark and hamsters squeak,
Are they really trying to speak?
When hens and roosters cluck and crow,
Are they really in the know?
Dear God, do animals talk to you
And tell you what they'd like to do?
For, if they can't, I'd like to say,
Please watch over them today.

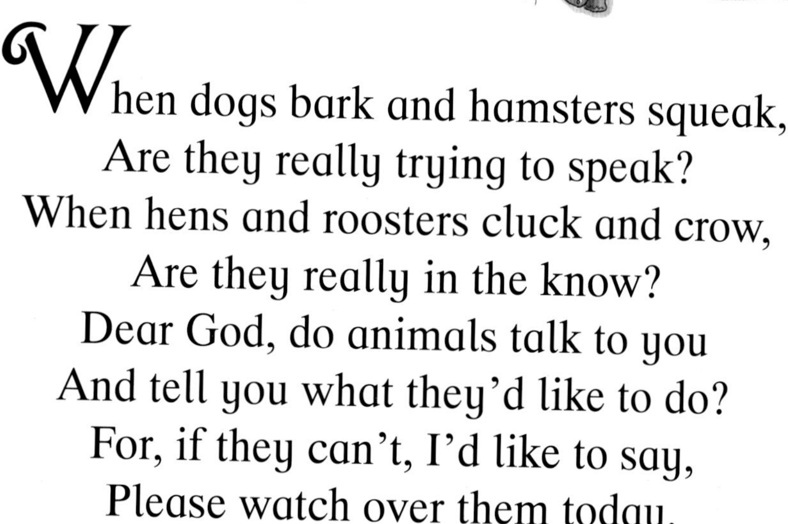

To all the humble beasts there be,
To all the birds on land and sea,
Great Spirit, sweet protection give
That free and happy they may live!

Thank you for the beasts so tall,
Thank you for the creatures small.
Thank you for all things that live,
Thank you, God, for all you give.

Anonymous

Said the robin to the sparrow,
"I should really like to know
why these busy human people
seem to fret and worry so."
Said the sparrow to the robin,
"Friend, I think that it must be
that they have no heavenly Father
such as cares for you and me."

Traditional

A robin redbreast in a cage
Puts all heaven in a rage.

William Blake (1757–1827)

I heard a lark singing this morning.
He flew straight up into the blue sky,
singing for all he was worth.
Help me learn how to praise you,
Lord, as gladly as that lark.

The lark's on the wing;
the snail's on the thorn:
God's in his Heaven—
all's right with the world!

Robert Browning (1812–1889)

Dear Father, hear and bless
Thy beasts and singing birds,
And guard with tenderness
Small things that have no words.

Anonymous

I come in the little things,
saith the Lord: not borne on the
morning's wings of majesty, but I have
set my feet amidst the delicate
and bladed wheat.

I come in the little things,
saith the Lord: yea! On the glancing
wings of eager birds, the softly
pattering feet of furred and gentle beasts.

I come in the little things,
saith the Lord.

Evelyn Underhill (1875–1941)

My friend the tortoise
Doesn't say much,
He don't need a cage,
A nest, or a hutch.
He brings his own house
Wherever he goes,
Whatever he thinks about
Only God knows.

Dear God,
our pets are very special.
They give us love and
many happy hours.
They teach us how to love
and look after them.
Thank you.

I had a little puppy—
I fed him every day.
We'd play indoors
Or go for walks,
And run and jump and play.

That little puppy grew and grew
Till he was fully grown.
Now I am big
And he is too—
I thank God he's my own.

Our pets are our friends.
They let us know we're not alone.
So when they die, we are sad inside.
Help us in our sadness to remember
all the good things about our pets
and to thank you for them.

God bless the animals
Great and small,
And help us learn
To love them all.

There are so many creatures
All over the world
From the elephant to the gnu.
So many shapes
And colors and kinds,
So I say, dear God, thank you.

Here's my goldfish
Sweet and small,
She can't remember
Much at all.
So please help me
To remember
To give her food
And care for her.

Dear God,
I love to watch my gerbil running around,
eating his food, and scratching behind his ears.
Please help me look after him every day
so that he is a safe and happy gerbil.
Amen

Our little kitten
Never sleeps—
He rolls and jumps,
He runs and leaps.
But I am sure
This ball of fur
Is praising God
With every purr.

Please listen to this special prayer,
And if I start to cry,
It's because my budgie's sick
And I think he's going to die.
Nothing lives forever,
That is something I know.
But even though I know it,
I wish it wasn't so.

Lord, you have made
so many things!
How wisely you made
them all! The earth
is filled with your
creatures.

From Psalm 104

Praise God, from whom all blessings flow,
Praise him, all creatures here below,
Praise him above, ye heavenly host,
Praise Father, Son, and Holy Ghost.

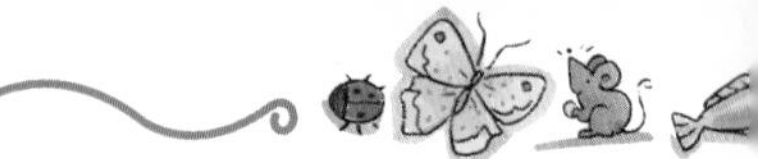

All creatures of our God and king,
Lift up your voice and with us sing
Alleluia, alleluia!

St. Francis of Assisi (c. 1225)

Oh heavenly Father, protect and bless all things that have breath: guard them from all evil and let them sleep in peace.

Albert Schweitzer (1875–1965)

Thank you, God, that I
can break my nighttime
fast with breakfast.
What a great way to
start a day!

Munch, munch, munch,
Thank you for our lunch.

Blessed art thou, Lord our God, king of the universe, who feeds the entire world in his goodness—with grace, with kindness, and with mercy. He gives food to all life, for his kindness is eternal. Blessed are you, God, who nourishes all.

Jewish blessing

Be present at our table, Lord;
Be here and everywhere adored.
Thy creatures bless, and grant that we
May feast in paradise with thee.

John Wesley (1703–1791)

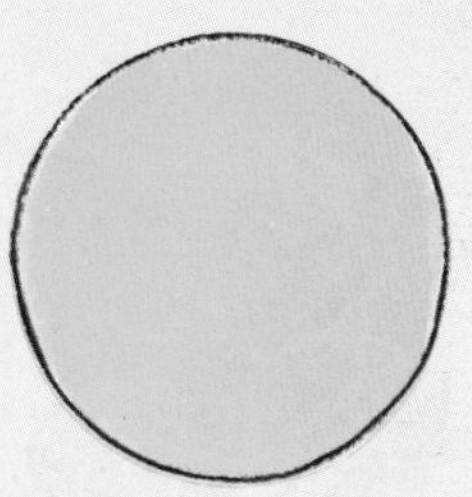

Oh, the Lord is good to me,
And so I thank the Lord
For giving me the things I need,
The sun, the rain, and the apple seed.
Oh, the Lord is good to me.

John Chapman, "Johnny Appleseed," (1774–1845)

Blessed art thou, oh Lord our God,
king of the universe, who bringest forth
bread from the earth.

Jewish blessing

Cows make milk
And bees make honey.
Farmers cut corn
When it's sunny.
Plums and apples
Grow on trees.
And in Dad's garden
Are beans and peas.
Thank you, God,
For the food I eat,
For fruit and milk
And bread and meat.
If it wasn't for
These gifts from you
I really don't know what we'd do!

Dear God,
Thank you for all the wonderful food
And letting me taste it.
Help me think of others, too,
And not to waste it.

Thank you, Father God, for our food,
and thank you for those who have prepared it.

Red tomato,
Orange carrot,
Yellow pepper,
Lettuce green,
Beets that have blue and purple
Indigo and violet sheen.
Thank you, God, that in my salad
Rainbow colors can be seen.

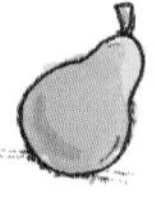

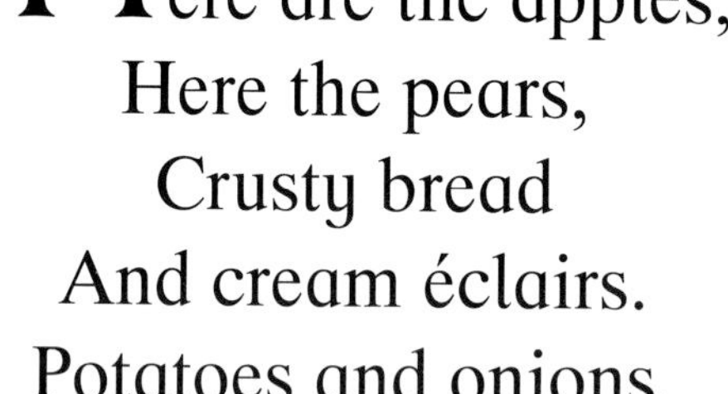

Here are the apples,
Here the pears,
Crusty bread
And cream éclairs.

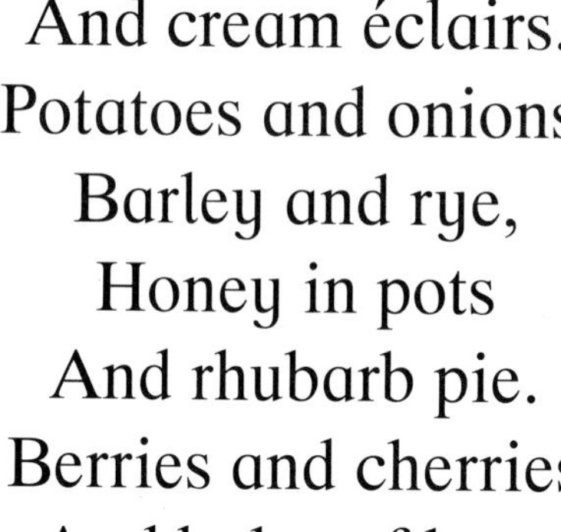

Potatoes and onions,
Barley and rye,
Honey in pots
And rhubarb pie.
Berries and cherries
And bales of hay,

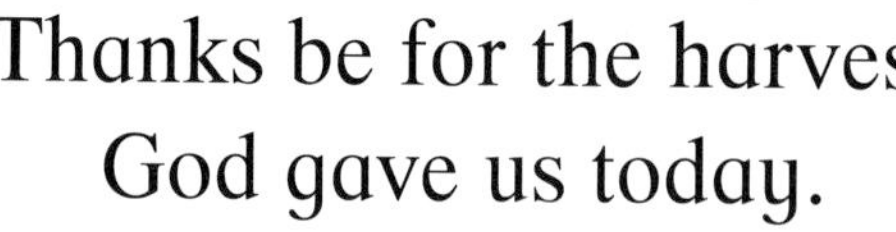

Thanks be for the harvest
God gave us today.

Somebody sowed it, somebody watered,
Somebody weeded and hoed,
And God gave the sun, the wind, and the rain
To bring us this harvest of food.

Us and this; God bless.

Quaker prayer

The bread is warm and fresh,
The water cool and clear.
Lord of all life, be with us,
Lord of all life, be near.

African grace

God is great,
God is good,
Let us thank him
For this food.

Anonymous

Thank you, God,
for this day, this family,
and this food.

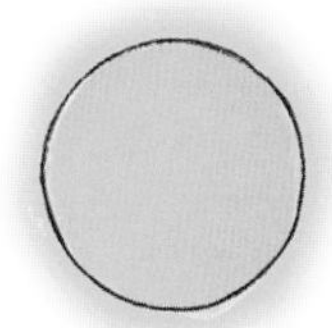

Morning is here,
The board is spread.
Thanks be to God,
Who gives us bread.

Anonymous

Thank you for the precious food
I eat three times a day.
I know some children will not
Have enough to eat today.
I wish that I could help them,
But I don't know what to do.
Please, God, will you make sure
That they have three meals, too?

Jesus fed the multitude
On five loaves and two fishes.
We don't know how he did it
But, Jesus, bless these dishes!

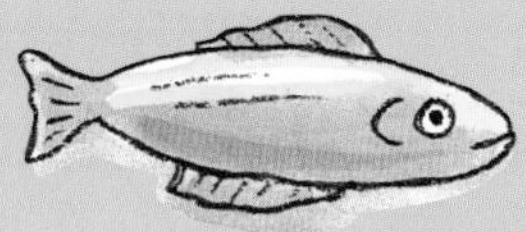

Father, as we enjoy the food that gives
us strength, help us remember those
who have less than we do. May we pay attention
to what's going on in the world
and use our strength and money
to help in any way we can.

Dear God,
Help me share
All that you have given me
With your children
Everywhere.

Jesus, you fed many people with only
five loaves of bread and two fishes.
Help us to share what we have with others.

May we who have much
remember those who have little.
May we who are full remember those
who are hungry. May we who are
loved remember those who are lonely.
May we who are safe remember those
who are in danger. May we who have
so much learn to share.

Dear God, thank you for
this drink of water. Thank you for its
clear sparkle, and that it is fresh and clean.
Help me remember those who have no
clean water to drink. Help us do all
we can to help them.

Peace be to this house
and to all who dwell here.
Peace be to those that enter
and to those that depart.

Anonymous

Oh God, make the door of this house wide enough to receive all who need human love and fellowship, and a heavenly Father's care; and narrow enough to shut out all envy, pride, and hate. Make its threshold smooth enough to be no stumbling block to children, nor to straying feet, but rugged enough to turn back the tempter's power: make it a gateway to thine eternal kingdom.

Bishop Thomas Ken (1637–1711)

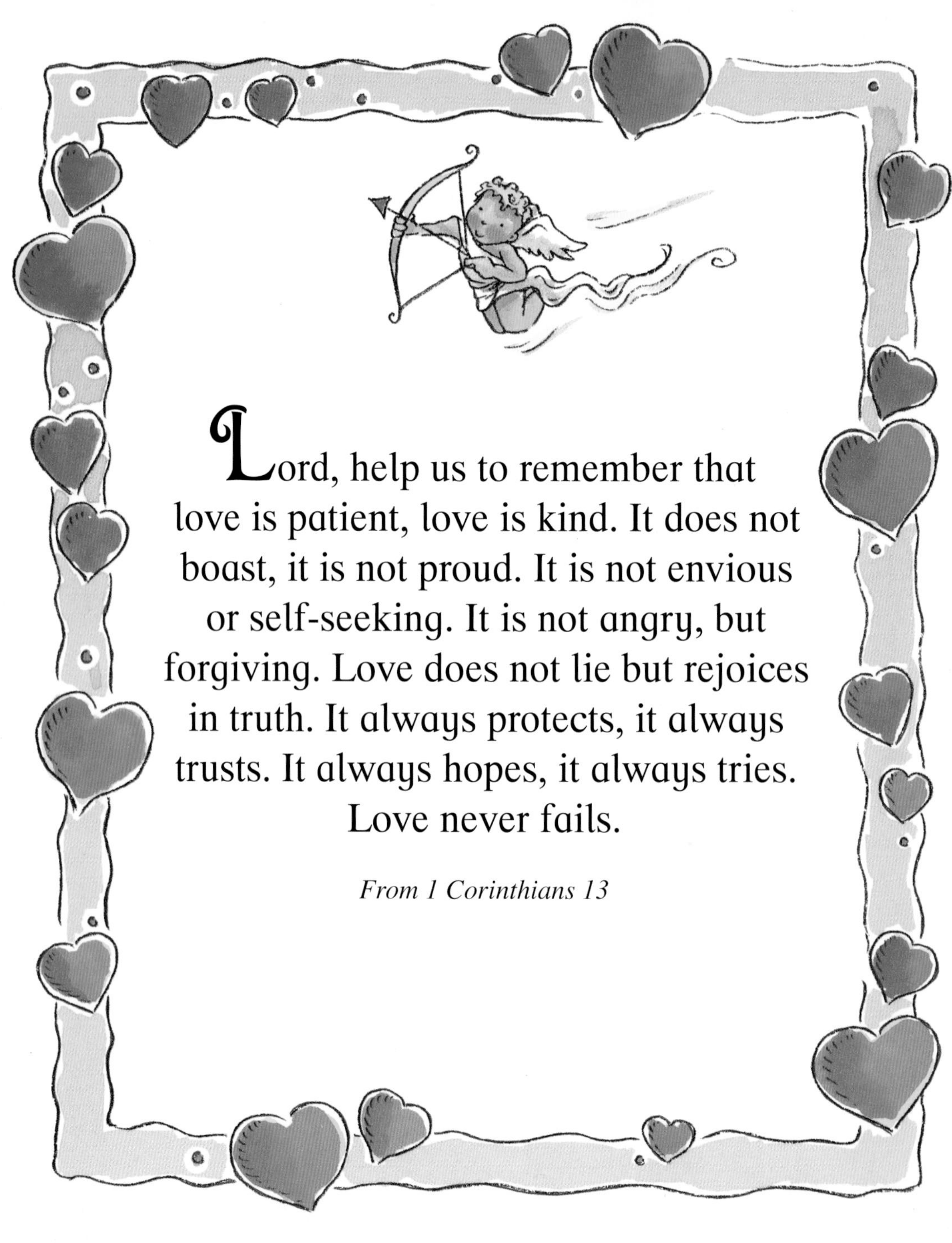

Lord, help us to remember that love is patient, love is kind. It does not boast, it is not proud. It is not envious or self-seeking. It is not angry, but forgiving. Love does not lie but rejoices in truth. It always protects, it always trusts. It always hopes, it always tries. Love never fails.

From 1 Corinthians 13

God bless you,
God bless me,
And keep us safe
As safe can be.

Dear Lord Jesus, when you came into the world you had no home. Mary and Joseph had to travel to a strange town and lay you in a manger in a stable. Please help all the people who are homeless today or who have to travel far from their homes. Help us think about how we, who have homes, can help them and remember them.

Thank you for visits
And all kinds of treats.
Thank you for walking
Down different streets.
Thank you for good times
Wherever we roam.
But most of all, God,
Thank you for home.

Jesus bless our home today,
Be known in all we do and say.
When there's trouble, be our guide,
Bless everyone who steps inside.

Jesus said, “Let the little children come to me, for the kingdom of God belongs to such as these.”

Matthew 19:14; Mark 10:14; Luke 18:16

Dear Lord, I love my little bed
Where I can lay my tired head.
It's great to have a place to be
Where there is only you and me.

God bless this mess,
But make me strong
To put things back
Where they belong!

My mom does so many special things,
There's no end to the joy she brings.
She buys my clothes, cooks food I like,
She comforts me when I fall off my bike.
I love her more than I can say
And try to show her every day!

When we go out my dad says,
"Son, don't run,

Look around you, listen hard,
Walk, don't talk."

We see everything all around us
From trees to bees.

Thank you, God, for my dad.
Tell him I love him.

Thank you Lord for grandmas and grandpas. Thank you for the stories they tell us and the things they help us make. Thank you that they have time to tie our shoelaces and take us for walks. Please bless them all.

Grandma sits me on her knee,
Strokes my hair and sings to me.
Grandpa jokes and likes to play ball,
And picks me up when I fall.

At dinner Grandpa likes to cook
While Grandma sits and reads a book.
I love them, Lord, and pray that they
Will be there for me every day.

Dear God, thank you for my family and the things we do together. Thank you for the meals we eat, for the jokes we share, for the TV we watch, for the place where we live. Help us remember that we are part of your family.

Look after my family when we have to be apart. Thank you for the thoughts we share, the phone calls we make, the messages we send, the memories we keep, the prayers we pray. Help us remember that you are with us all.

Thank you,
God, that everyone belongs
to your family; you are our
Father, we are your children.
Thank you, God, for the
worldwide family of your people.
Thank you for our brothers
and sisters the whole
world over.

Neighbors, everybody needs good neighbors. Please God bless mine, and help me be a good neighbor, too.

We commend unto you, Oh Lord,
our souls and our bodies, our minds and our
thoughts, our prayers and our hopes, our health
and our work, our life and our death, our parents
and brothers and sisters, our benefactors and
friends, our neighbors, our countrymen, and
all Christian folk, this day and always.

Lancelot Andrews (1555–1626)

Father God, bless me and my family.
Dear Jesus, keep my family and me.
Holy Spirit, guard us all.
Great God, keep us in the circle
of your love.

Josie is my best friend;
She's never rude or cruel.
Jimmy is the tallest,
And he thinks he's really cool.
Jason wears a white shirt,
And gets his math all right.
Alice is the sweetest,
Her curls are small and tight.
All my friends are special,
They mean a lot to me.
And Jesus is my friend as well
Because he cares for me.

Sometimes I'm up, sometimes down,
My thoughts are like a seesaw.
But I thank God you're always there—
That's what friends are for.

I have
quiet friends,
noisy friends,
funny ones and sad,
many friends,
few friends,
sensible and mad,
good friends,
naughty friends,
tall friends and short;
thank you, God,
for giving me
friends of every sort.

Sometimes it's not easy to make friends, dear God.
Help me begin by being friendly to others.

The Bible says, don't let the sun go down on your anger. Dear Lord, when I have a fight with my friend, help us make up before we leave each other, because it will be much harder to say sorry the next day.

Oh God,
I feel so bad,
I said some things
I shouldn't have.
I want to start
Again and say
With all my heart
I'm sorry.

Father God, who gave me life,
help me live for you.

Teach me, my God and king,
In all things thee to see,
That what I do in anything
To do it as for thee.

George Herbert (1593–1632)

Guide us, teach us, and strengthen us, oh Lord, we beseech thee, until we become such as thou would'st have us be: pure, gentle, truthful, high-minded, courteous, generous, able, dutiful, and useful; for thy honor and glory.

Charles Kingsley (1819–1875)

Lord, teach me all that I should know;
In grace and wisdom I may grow;
The more I learn to do thy will,
The better may I love thee still.

Isaac Watts (1674–1748)

Oh Lord, let us not live to be useless,
for Christ's sake.

John Wesley (1703–1788)

Lord, may your spirit
Be nearer than breathing,
Nearer than any part,
Nearer to me than my own two feet;
May you live within my heart.

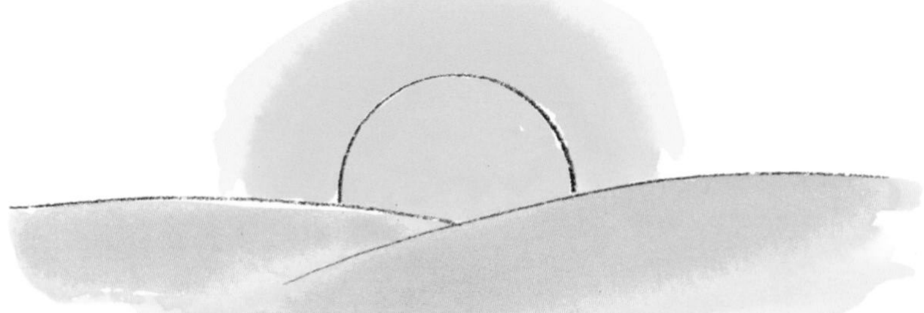

Day by day, dear Lord, of thee
Three things I pray:
To see thee more clearly,
To love thee more dearly,
To follow thee more nearly,
Day by day.

St. Richard of Chichester (1197–1253)

Every day with Jesus
Is a special day.
Jesus, help me always
To walk your way.

Every day I thank you Lord,
I'm very glad I live,
Help me to pass on the joy
That knowing you can give.

Father, help me see the world as you see it,
help me live in the world as you would live,
help me care about the world in all its troubles,
help me play my part in making it better.

Oh God, make us children of
quietness and heirs of peace.

St. Clement

Make me pure, Lord: thou art holy;
Make me meek, Lord: thou wert lowly.

Gerard Manley Hopkins (1844–1889)

God our Father, creator of the world,
please help us love one another.
Make nations friendly with other nations;
make all of us love one another like brothers
and sisters. Help us do our part to bring peace
in the world and happiness to all people.

Prayer from Japan

Last night, when I went to sleep,
I prayed that you would help me keep
A promise that I made to Mom
Not to be so quarrelsome.

I've really tried so hard today
To keep the promise, come what may.
And, Jesus, you will never guess
I think I've done it, more or less!

Dear God,
I think I'll help more
And give my mom some pleasure.
I'll straighten up my bedroom
And be her "little treasure."

I offer thee
Every flower that ever grew,
Every bird that ever flew,
Every wind that ever blew,
Good God.

I offer thee
Every flake of virgin snow,
Every spring of earth below,
Every human joy and woe,
My Love!

Irish prayer

Dear God,
when I feel like a nobody,
help me remember that
I am somebody to you.

Do other children help much?
Please tell me if they do,
And I'll make a special effort
For Mom and Dad and you.

Lord, make my heart a place
where angels sing!

John Keble (1792–1866)

Oh make my heart so still, so still,
When I am deep in prayer,
That I might hear the white mist-wreaths
Losing themselves in air!

Utsonomya San, Japan

Dear God,
I'm going to really try
To be good as gold all day,
And nice to all my special friends
When I go out to play.
If they say nasty things to me
I mustn't do the same.
I don't want Mom to get annoyed,
Or worse—give me the blame!
But, God, it isn't easy
To be as nice as pie,
So I know that you will help me
To really, really try!

Dear God, I love secrets.
Help me know when I should keep a secret and when I should tell a secret.
And help me understand the difference between the two.

Move our hearts with the calm,
smooth flow of your grace. Let the river
of your love run through our souls.
May my soul be carried by the current of your
love, toward the wide, infinite ocean of heaven.

Gilbert of Hoyland (12th century)

This is me
looking up at you.
Help me always be
close to you.

Teach me to do the thing that's right,
And when I sin, forgive,
And make it still my chief delight
To serve thee while I live.

Jane Taylor (1783–1824)

Help me notice when people need a hand. Help me see when they are sad and need a friend.

Keep me from being
Too busy to see
When someone needs help
From someone like me.

Drive from me every temptation and danger,
surround me on the sea of unrighteousness,
and in the narrows, crooks, and straits,
keep thou my coracle, keep it always.

From Carmina Gadelica

Dear God, today started badly and got worse, like a drawing that went wrong. Help me bring the drawing to you so that you can rub it out and give me a clean sheet of paper for tomorrow.

Sometimes I'm good,
But I can be bad.
Sometimes I'm happy,
Sometimes I'm sad.

I can be helpful,
I can be mean.
Sometimes I'm somewhere
In between.
Help me do what I know I should do.
Help me choose to be good like you.

Gentle Jesus, hear me,
Will you please be near me,
I don't want to be alone,
Feeling sad all on my own.
Tomorrow will be different
At the start of a new day,
But until the morning comes,
Stay close to me, I pray.

Oh God, as truly as you are
our father, so just as truly you are
our mother. We thank you, God our
father, for your strength and goodness.
We thank you, God our mother,
for the closeness of your caring.
Oh God, we thank you for the great
love you have for each one of us.

Julian of Norwich (1343–1413)

Oh God, help us not to despise or oppose what we do not understand.

William Penn (1644–1718)

Help me to know
What's wrong and what's right;
Help me to do good
With all my might.

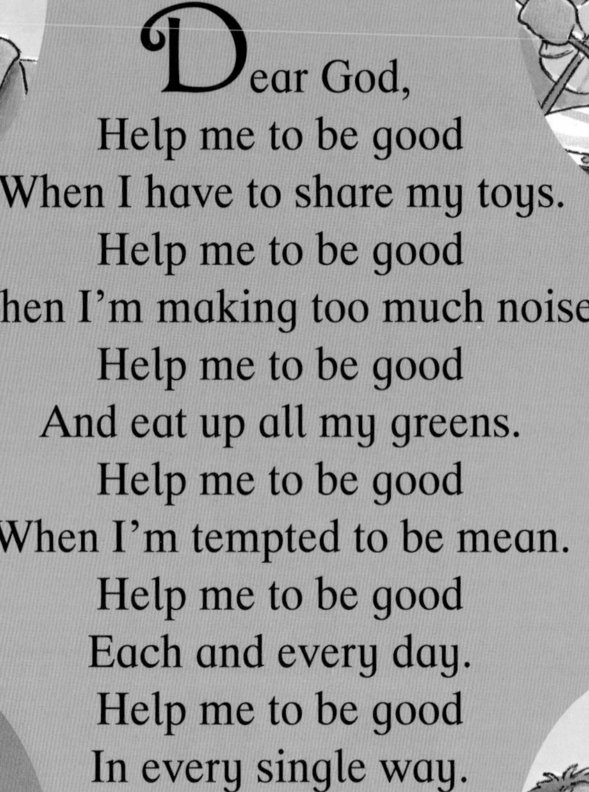

Dear God,
Help me to be good
When I have to share my toys.
Help me to be good
When I'm making too much noise.
Help me to be good
And eat up all my greens.
Help me to be good
When I'm tempted to be mean.
Help me to be good
Each and every day.
Help me to be good
In every single way.

When I feel blue,
Give me something to do
For somebody else
Who is feeling sad, too.

When I feel small and quite alone,
I know I'm not.
Because, dear God, I know you're there—
It helps a lot!

Now thank we all our God
With hearts and hands and voices
Who wondrous things hath done,
In whom this world rejoices;
Who from our mother's arms
Hath blessed us on our way
With countless gifts of love,
And still is ours today.

Martin Rinkart (1586–1649)

Good Morning

Our Father in heaven,
Hallowed be your name.
Your kingdom come,
Your will be done,
On earth as it is in heaven.
Give us today our daily bread,
And forgive us our sins,
As we forgive those who sin against us.
Lead us away from temptation
And deliver us from evil,
For yours is the kingdom,
And the power, and the glory,
Forever and ever.
Amen

The prayer that Jesus taught his friends

My Father, for another night
Of quiet sleep and rest,
For all the joy of morning light,
Your holy name be blest.

Henry William Baker (1821–1877)

In the quiet of the morning,
be still and know that God is near.

Adapted from Psalm 46

Something's gone wrong with this morning,
My pillow seems stuck to my head!
I'm in a bad mood,
I've gone right off my food,
And I don't want to get out of bed.

Dear God, can you help with this morning?
I really don't want to be sad.
Though the morning is gray,
This is a new day,
So perhaps things aren't really so bad!

Whatever I do and
wherever I go, be with me,
Lord, this day.

Lord, be with us this day.
Within us to purify us;
above us to draw us up;
beneath us to sustain us;
before us to lead us;
behind us to restrain us;
around us to protect us.

St. Patrick (389–461)

Good morning, good morning,
Praise to you each morning,
Good morning, good morning to you!

All that we see rejoices in the sunshine,
All that we hear makes merry in the spring:
God grant us such a mind
To be glad after our kind,
And to sing his praises evermore for everything.

Christina Rossetti (1830–1894)

I go forth today
in the might of heaven,
in the brightness of the sun,
in the whiteness of snow,
in the splendor of fire,
in the speed of lightning,
in the swiftness of wind,
in the firmness of rock.
I go forth today
in the hand of God.

Irish prayer (8th century)

Christ be with me and within me;
Christ behind me;
Christ to win me;
Christ to comfort and restore me;
Christ beneath me;
Christ above me;
Christ in quiet and in danger;
Christ in hearts of all that love me;
Christ in mouth of friend and stranger.

St. Patrick (389–461)

God be in my head, and in my understanding; God be in my eyes, and in my looking; God be in my mouth, and in my speaking; God be in my heart, and in my thinking; God be at my end, and at my departing.

The Sarum Primer

Oh great Chief, light a candle within my heart that I may see what is therein and sweep the rubbish from your dwelling place.

Prayer from Africa

Come into my soul, Lord,
as the dawn breaks into the sky;
let your sun rise in my heart
at the coming of the day.

Traditional

This is the morning, clear and bright,
This is the break of day.
This is the last gray strands of night,
This is the time to pray.

Dear God, this is a new day.
Help me learn from yesterday's
mistakes and do better today.

I've washed my face
And brushed my teeth
And combed my hair right through,
And so dear Lord
I'm ready now
To face this day with you.

I bind unto myself today
The power of God to hold and lead,
His eye to watch, his might to stay,
His ear to hearken to my need;
The wisdom of my God to teach,
His hand to guide, his shield to ward;
The word of God to give me speech,
His heavenly host to be my guard.

St. Patrick (389–461)

Dear God, please bless
In park or street
The people I see.
Dear God, this day
Bless me to them
And them to me.

Traditional

Oh Lord, thou knowest how busy I must be this day;
if I forget thee, do not thou forget me.

Sir Jacob Astley (before the battle of Edgehill, 1642)

Dear God, today may be hard
with lots to do and not much time.
Help me keep calm and
tackle each job as it comes.
Help me know that you are with me
when I'm too busy to think of you.

The things, good Lord, that we pray for, give us grace to work for; through Jesus Christ our Lord.

Sir Thomas More (1478–1535)

Let us with a gladsome mind
Praise the Lord for he is kind;
For his mercies shall endure,
Ever faithful, ever sure.

John Milton (1608–1674)

Dear God, this is Monday.
Help me start a good week.

Dear God, it's Tuesday.
It's still early in the week.
Be with me as I try to make it
a good one.

Dear God, Wednesday already!
Halfway through the week.
Please bless all those I meet today.

Dear God, thank you for Thursday. I've made a good start. Please help me with the rest of the week.

Dear God, it's Friday.
Nearly the weekend! Time to look back on my week. Thank you for being with me.

Dear God, it's Saturday—yippeee!
So much to do, so little time.
Please bless all my friends today.

Dear God, it's Sunday, your day.
Happy day. Holy day. Thank you for the past week. Please help me enjoy next week with you.

Sunday should be a fun day,
Not a glum day.
Sunday should be a rest day,
Not a work day.

When God finished making the world,
he had a rest, put up his feet,
and said, “That’s good!”
Dear God, thank you for this Sunday.
Help us rest and play, celebrate
and say, “That’s good!”

Here is the church,

(link hands)

Here is the steeple,

(put index fingers together)

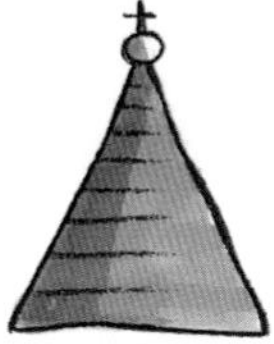

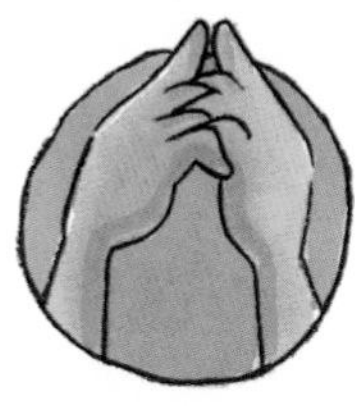

Look inside,

(keeping your hands linked, turn them upside down)

Here are the people!

(wiggle your fingers)

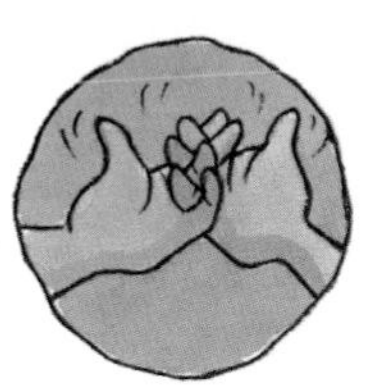

Traditional

Bless the bride and bless the groom
In every kind of weather.
Bless their love and bless their home
And all their life together.

Special baby, we gather around
to welcome you into God's family,
the church.

We will always be here for you
as brothers and sisters and
children of God.

Lord Jesus, thank you for making me.
Thank you for loving me, thank you for
calling me to follow you.
In this confirmation service, I give
myself back to you in love and joy.
Help me to live for you and for others
with the help of your Holy Spirit,
today and every day.

Lord, you know that we are sad today because someone we loved very much has died. Today is a day to say goodbye and to hand them into your care. Help us to know that they are at peace with you, and that one day we will see them again in heaven.

These candles on my cake,
I blow them out,
A wish I make.
To this wish
I add a prayer:
Please God, be with me
Everywhere.

We're off on vacation. Oh what fun!
There may be rain or there may be sun.
But we'll all have a lovely time together,
And thank you, God, whatever the weather!

Today is a day to remember—
I finally pulled out my loose tooth!
I feel more grown-up already.
Thank you, God, for special
days to remember.

We've been packing our stuff,
We've been counting the days,
We've been saying goodbye
In a whole lot of ways.
It's a very special day—we're moving!

Please travel with us
As we leave our old home,
Please help us to know
That we're never alone.
It's a very special day—WE'RE MOVING!

Come, thou long-expected Jesus,
Born to set thy people free,
From our fears and sins release us,
Let us find our rest in thee.

Charles Wesley (1707–1788)

Away in a manger, no crib for a bed,
The little Lord Jesus laid down his sweet head.
The stars in the bright sky looked down where he lay,
The little Lord Jesus asleep on the hay.

Be near me, Lord Jesus; I ask thee to stay
Close by me forever, and love me, I pray.
Bless all the dear children in thy tender care,
And fit us for heaven, to live with thee there.

Traditional

Happy Birthday, Jesus!
Thank you for sharing your special day
with us. The kings brought you gifts,
so we give presents. Your family was happy,
so we have parties and food.
Thank you for giving us Christmas.
Happy Birthday, Jesus!

Love came down at Christmas,
Love all lovely, love divine;
Love was born at Christmas,
Star and angels gave the sign.

Christina Rossetti (1830–1894)

Lord Jesus, wise men brought
you gifts when you were born:
gold, frankincense, and myrrh.
They were a sign that you would
be a king, a prophet, and a savior.
Thank you for the presents
we give each other at Christmas.
May they always be a sign of love.

Dear God, as I stand at the door
Of this new year with you,
Help me to take your hand
And to walk through,
Trusting that you
Will be with me always
In everything I think
And do and say.

This is a time for giving things up, so we remember how many good things we have.

This is a time for taking things up, so we remember to give good things to others.

Pancakes are yummy, but after today
We won't eat pancakes for many a day.
We're taking some time out
To think about things,
And we're waiting for Easter
When everyone sings.
Hallelujah!

Ash gray,
Sad day,
Time to make amends
For all the things
We've failed to do
For family and friends.

Ash gray,
Hopeful day,
Thank you, God, that you
Forgive our sins
And give us time
To go and live for you.

Dear Lord Jesus, thank you for the special meal that you shared with your friends before you died on the cross. You took bread and said it was like your own body. You took wine, like your own blood, and invited them to share it with you. Thank you that we can share the same meal so many years later, and become your friends as well.

Dear Jesus, everyone thought you were dead. They took you down from the cross, with tears in their eyes, and buried you in a cave with a big stone outside. Then they went home—the saddest people on earth.

Later, they went back to take flowers, but they got such a shock. The stone was rolled away, the cave was empty, and you were walking in the garden. Then they were the happiest people on earth. No wonder we are happy at Easter. We know that you're alive and always will be.

Jesus, who died for me,
Help me to live for thee.

Holy Spirit, hear me,
Friend from heaven above,
You are ever near me,
Fill my heart with love.

God the Father, bless us;
God the Son, defend us;
God the Spirit, keep us now
and evermore.

A Celtic blessing

    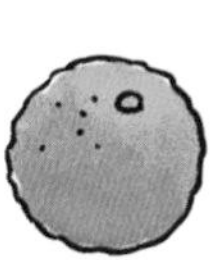  

 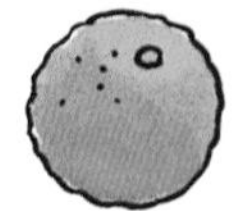

We plow the fields and scatter
The good seed on the land,
But it is fed and watered
By God's almighty hand:
He sends the snow in winter,
The warmth to swell the grain,
The breezes and the sunshine,
And soft refreshing rain.

All good gifts around us
Are sent from heaven above;
Then thank the Lord,
Oh thank the Lord
For all his love.

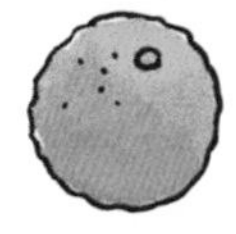 

Matthias Claudius (1740–1815)

    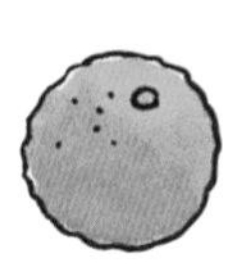  

The best part of the year is when you give us good things. Everywhere you go there is plenty. The fields in wild places pour out good things. All over the hills there is plenty. The fields are full of sheep. The valleys are full of grain. They seem to shout and sing for joy!

From Psalm 65

On Halloween
When ghosties fly
And spirits ply
Across the sky,
When children creep
Down lane and street
For trick or treat,
Keep us good Lord
From any harm
Or real alarm.
And may we be
Kept safe with thee
And home for tea!

Father we remember all the saints
who did great things for you and who are now
safe in your endless love. Help us to follow
their example, to do good things for others,
and one day to join them, with you, in heaven.

God bless my dad,
So strong and tall:
The bestest daddy
Of them all.

This is the thing
I want to say,
I love him loads
On Father's Day.

All the children of the world are friends,
so let us be friendly together, learn the
will of God, and do our best this day.
All the children of the world are friends.
Let us sing together joyously; let us praise
God loudly all this day.

Japanese prayer

Each day is new-baked, like a loaf of bread.
May we take it, smell it, taste and enjoy it,
and give thanks to the one who made it for us.

Start each day with a fresh beginning;
as if this whole world was made anew.

From an Amish school

Now the light has gone away,
Savior, listen while I pray,
Asking thee to watch and keep,
And to send me quiet sleep.

Frances Ridley Havergal (1836–1879)

Sleep, my child, and peace attend thee,
All through the night;
Guardian angels God will send thee,
All through the night.
Soft the drowsy hours are creeping,
Hill and vale in slumber sleeping,
I my loving vigil keeping,
All through the night.

Traditional Welsh prayer

Jesus, savior, wash away
All that has been wrong today:
Help me every day to be
Good and gentle, more like thee.

Frances Ridley Havergal (1836–1879)

Jesus tender shepherd, hear me,
Bless your little lamb tonight;
Through the darkness please be near me;
Keep me safe till morning light.

Mary Lundie Duncan (1814–1840)

Now I lay me down to sleep,
I pray the Lord my soul to keep.
If I should die before I wake,
I pray the Lord my soul to take.

Traditional

Lord, keep us safe this night,
Secure from all our fears;
May angels guard us while we sleep,
Till morning light appears.

John Leland (1754–1841)

God bless this house
From roof to floor,
The twelve apostles guard the door;
Four angels to my bed;
Gabriel stands at the head,
John and Peter at the feet,
All to watch me while I sleep.

Traditional

Father God, as the sun goes down
and I get ready for bed, other children
around the world are just waking up.
As you are with me through this night,
please be with them in their day.

Around our pillows golden ladders rise,
And up and down the skies,
With winged sandals shod,
The angels come and go;
The messengers of God!

Richard Henry Stoddard (1825–1903)

Matthew, Mark, Luke, and John,
Bless the bed that I lie on.
Four corners to my bed,
Four angels round my head,
One to watch and one to pray
And two to bear my soul away.

Traditional

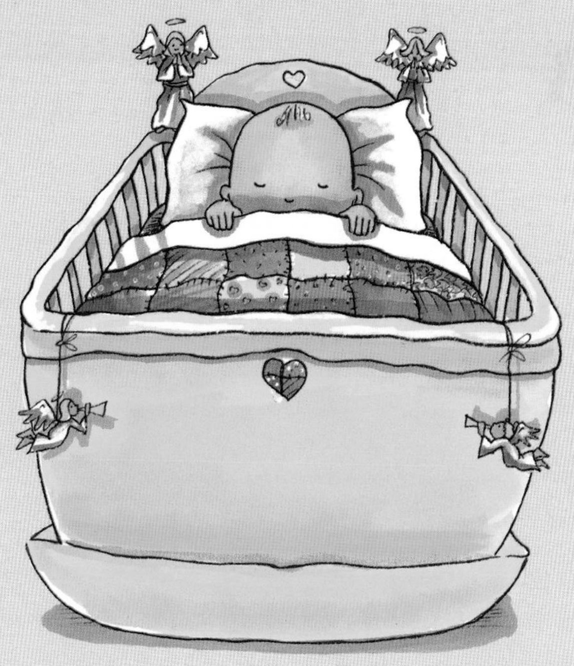

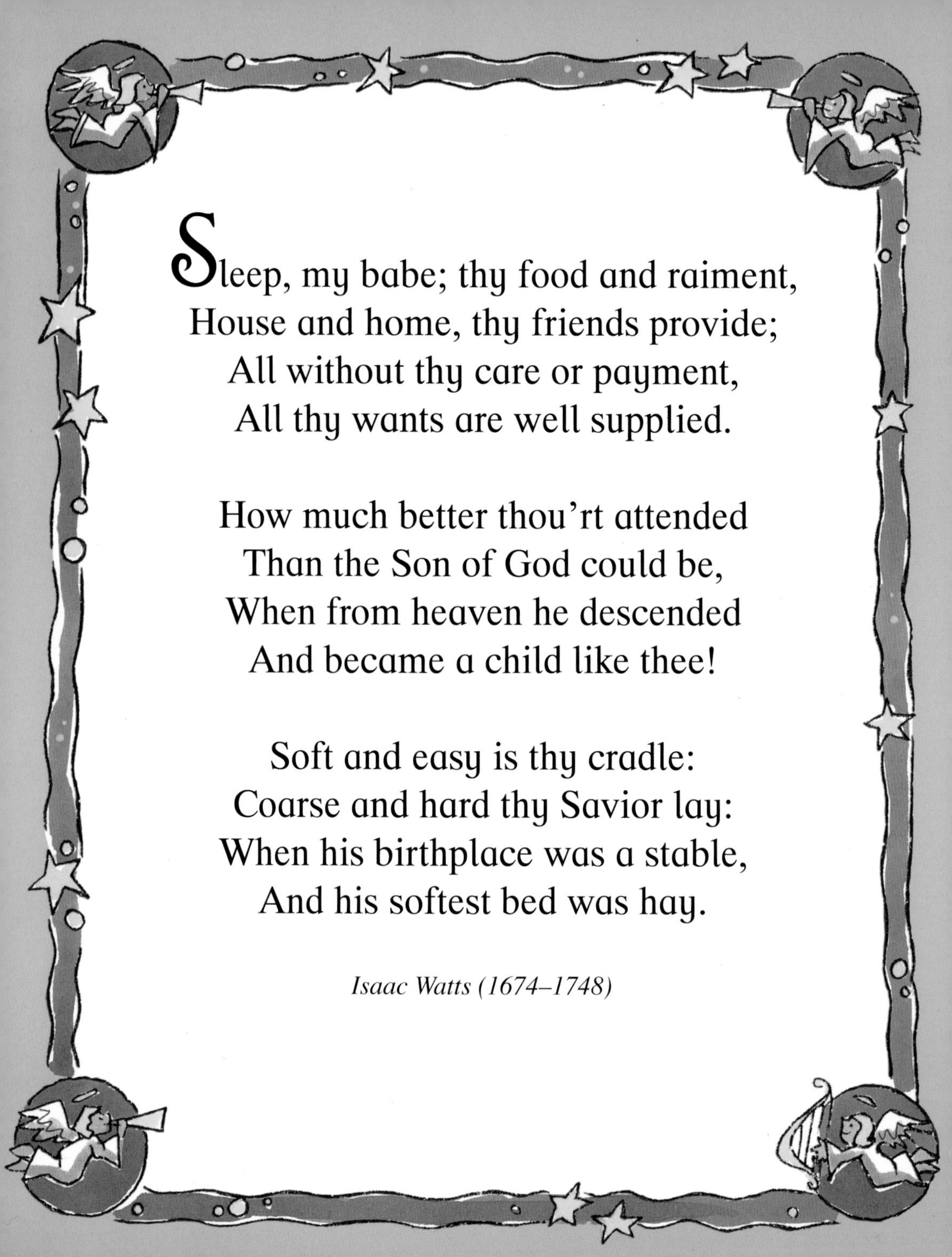

Sleep, my babe; thy food and raiment,
House and home, thy friends provide;
All without thy care or payment,
All thy wants are well supplied.

How much better thou'rt attended
Than the Son of God could be,
When from heaven he descended
And became a child like thee!

Soft and easy is thy cradle:
Coarse and hard thy Savior lay:
When his birthplace was a stable,
And his softest bed was hay.

Isaac Watts (1674–1748)

Keep watch, dear Lord, with those who work, or watch, or weep this night, and give your angels charge over those who sleep.

St. Augustine (354–430)

When I lie down, I go to sleep in peace; you alone, oh Lord, keep me perfectly safe.

From Psalm 4

Thank you God for a lovely day,
For sun and rain,
For work and play,
For all my family
And friends,
And for your love,
Which never ends.

Good night! Good night!
Far flies the light;
But still God's love
Shall flame above,
Making all bright.
Good night! Good night!

Victor Hugo (1802–1885)

Ah, dearest Jesus, holy child,
Make thee a bed, soft, undefiled
Within my heart, that it may be
A quiet chamber kept for thee.

Martin Luther (1483–1546)

I see the moon,
And the moon sees me;
God bless the moon
And God bless me.
Anonymous

The moon shines bright,
The stars give light
Before the break of day;
God bless you all,
Both great and small,
And send a joyful day.

Traditional

Dear God,
I'm staying over with my friend tonight,
We'll have a terrific time and not fight.
We'll eat too much, we'll jump on beds and have a lark.
So when you come to look for me and it's dark,
I won't be in my bed,
I'll be with my friend instead.

I'm sleeping at my grandma's
And I miss my mom and dad.
But Grandma cooked my favorite dinner
And now I'm not so sad!

I like to sleep at Grandma's;
She says it makes her glad.
Please, God, bless my grandma
And bless my mom and dad.

God bless Dad,
God bless Mom,
God bless me
and everyone.

Dear Father, thank you for today. There were good parts I'd like to remember and bad parts I'd rather forget. Forgive me for the things I did wrong and help me to be better tomorrow. Thank you for all the good things and thank you for being with me in it all.

God bless everyone in
the whole wide world tonight.
Guard us and guide us and help
us love one another, so that your
world can be a happy and peaceful
place for all people.

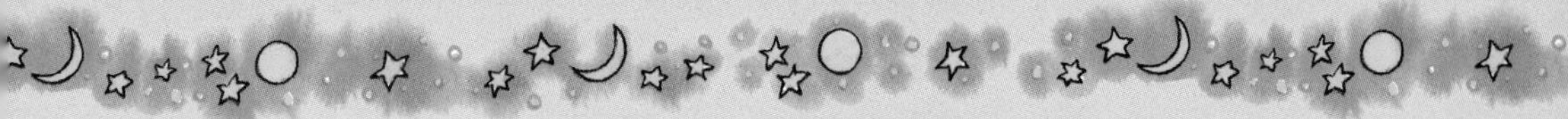

Day is done,
Gone the sun
From the lake,
From the hills,
From the sky.
Safely rest,
All is well!
God is nigh.

Traditional

Sleep little baby,
Soundly sleep,
Safe in my arms
My watch I'll keep,

And wing my prayer
To God above,
Who watches over us
With love.

Tend your sick ones, oh Lord Jesus Christ; rest your weary ones; bless your dying ones; soothe your suffering ones; pity your afflicted ones; shield your joyous ones; and all for your love's sake.

St. Augustine (354–430)

When I put my hands together,
When I say a prayer,
When I stop and say your name
You are there.

When I'm frightened of the dark,
When I've had a scare,
When I think I'm all alone
You are there.

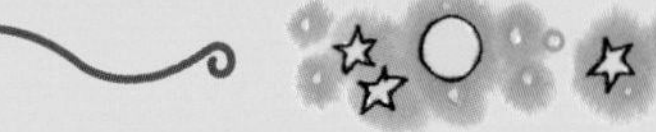

Jesus, please be near me
As I lie in bed tonight,
There's a dark place in the corner
And it's giving me a fright!
Mom says it's just a shadow,
And shadows are thin air,
But I can see it grinning,
And it's sitting in my chair!
Please shine your light, dear Jesus,
So that I can see
The shadow's really nothing
Now that you are close to me.

Alone with none but thee, my God,
I journey on my way.
What need I fear, when thou art near
Oh king of night and day?
More safe am I within thy hand
Than if a host did round me stand.

St. Columba (521–597)

Send peace into my heart, oh Lord,
that I may be contented with your mercies
of this day and confident of your protection for
this night; and having forgiven others, even as
you forgive me, may I go to my rest in peaceful
trust through Jesus Christ our Lord.

St. Francis of Assisi (1181–1226)

Peace of the running waves to you,
Deep peace of the flowing air to you,
Deep peace of the quiet earth to you,
Deep peace of the shining stars to you,
Deep peace of the shades of night to you,
Moon and stars always giving light to you.
Deep peace of Christ, the Son of Peace, to you.

Traditional Gaelic blessing

In winter, all the creatures 36
I offer thee 239
I peeked through the curtain 34
I pray that ordinary bread 127
I see the moon 354
I thank God for my rabbit 69
It is very nice to think 146
It's time to sleep 374
I've washed my face 287
Jesus bless our home today 162
Jesus fed the multitude 148
Jesus, friend of little children 204
Jesus, may I walk your way 248
Jesus our brother, strong and good 60
Jesus, please be near me 366
Jesus said, "Let the little children come to me" 163
Jesus, savior, wash away 340
Jesus tender shepherd, hear me 341
Jesus, who died for me 323
Jesus, you fed many people 151
Josie is my best friend 206
Joy to the world! 39
Just a glass of warm milk 125
Keep me from being too busy to see 254
Keep watch, dear Lord, with those 349
Last night, when I went to sleep 237
Let us with a gladsome mind 293
Let the words of my mouth 281
Little lamb, who made thee? 68
Look after my family 195
Lord behold our family here assembled 197
Lord, be with us this day 271
Lord, help us to remember 158
Lord Jesus, thank you for making me 306
Lord Jesus, wise men brought 316
Lord, keep us safe this night 343
Lord, make me see your glory 58
Lord, make my heart a place 242
Lord, may your spirit 229
Lord, teach me all that I should know 227
Lord thy glory fills the heaven 42
Lord, when we have not any light 338
Lord, you have made so many things! 108
Lord, you know that we are sad 307
Love came down at Christmas 315
Love is giving, not taking 212
Love is giving your last treat to a friend 213
Loving Shepherd of thy sheep 82
Lo, the winter is past, the rain is over 71

Make me pure, Lord: thou art holy 235
Matthew, Mark, Luke, and John 347
May our friendship last 217
May the road rise to meet you 220
May we who have much 152
Me and my dog 107
Morning is here 144
Move our hearts with the calm 246
Munch, munch, munch 113
My aunt and uncle live very far away 189
My Father, for another night 267
My friend the tortoise 94
My mom does so many special things 168
My mom's mom is called my grandma 186
Neighbors, everybody needs good neighbors 201
No shop does the bird use 80
Now I lay me down to sleep 342
Now the light has gone away 336
Now thank we all our God 265
Oh God, help us not to despise or oppose 260
Oh God, I feel so bad 211
Oh God, make the door of this house 157
Oh God, make us children of quietness 234
Oh God, as truly as you are 259
Oh God! who giv'st the winter's cold 37
Oh gracious and holy Father 249
Oh great Chief 279
Oh heavenly Father, protect and bless 111
Oh, the Lord is good to me 128
Oh Lord, let us not live to be useless 228
Oh Lord, thou knowest how busy I must be this day 290
Oh make my heart so still, so still 243
Oh, thought I! 31
Once I was a baby 173
On Halloween 328
Our Father in heaven 266
Our little kitten 104
Our pets are our friends 97
Pancakes are yummy 319
Peace be to this house 156
Peace of the running waves to you 369
Pizzas and burgers, a plate of hot dogs 124
Please God, you know how much we love 106
Please listen to this special prayer 105
Praise God, from whom all blessings flow 109
Praise the Lord from the heavens 46
Praise the Lord! Praise him on earth 43

Praise the Lord! Ye heavens adore him 40
Red tomato 133
Roses are red 29
Said the robin to the sparrow 88
School is over 55
School lunches can taste nasty 123
Send peace into my heart, oh Lord 368
Sleep little baby 362
Sleep, my babe; thy food and raiment 348
Sleep, my child, and peace attend thee 337
Snowdrops 35
Somebody sowed it, somebody watered 137
Some hae meat and canna eat 147
Something's gone wrong with this morning 269
Sometimes I'm good 257
Sometimes I'm up, sometimes down 207
Sometimes it's not easy to make friends 209
Special baby, we gather round 305
Start each day with a fresh beginning 335
Summer suns are glowing 26
Sunday should be a fun day 301
Teach me, my God and king 223
Teach me to do the thing that's right 250
Teach us, Lord, to serve you as you deserve 225
Teach us to fix our thoughts on thee 252
Tend your sick ones, oh Lord 363
Thank you, Father God, for our food 132
Thank you for the beasts so tall 87
Thank you for flowers 49
Thank you for my dinner 115
Thank you for Nan 182
Thank you for the precious food 145
Thank you for the special time 30
Thank you for visits 161
Thank you God for all the different people 180
Thank you, God, for giving us 64
Thank you God for a lovely day 351
Thank you, God, for my friends at church 218
Thank you, God, for showing me 8
Thank you, God, for this day 143
Thank you, God, that everyone belongs to your family 200
Thank you, God, that I can break my nighttime fast 112
Thank you, God, that looking after our pets 102
Thank you, God, that the world is wide 63

Thank you Lord for grannies 184
The best part of the year 327
The Bible says, don't let the sun go down 210
The bread is warm and fresh 141
The chameleon can change his color 85
The grace of the Lord Jesus Christ 373
The green land stretches to the sea 21
The lark's on the wing 91
The little cares that fretted me 67
The moon shines bright 355
The rooster crows at break of day 277
There are so many creatures 99
The sea is Christ's 76
These candles on my cake 308
The snail does the holy will of God 84
The song of the wren 70
The things, good Lord, that we pray for 292
The worm is very plain 78
The year's at the spring 24
This is the day that the Lord has made 276
This is me 247
This is the morning, clear and bright 283
This is a time for giving things up 318
To all the humble beasts there be 86
Today is a day to remember 310
Tomorrow is a special day 22
Two eyes to see, two ears to hear 51
Two of us sharing 214
Us and this 140
We can praise God on the trumpet 41
We commend unto you, Oh Lord 202
We plow the fields and scatter 326
We pray, Lord, for the humble beasts 77
We're off on vacation 309
We've been packing our stuff 311
We've got a new baby 175
What can I give him 224
Whatever I do 270
When astronauts look back at our world 18
When dogs bark and hamsters squeak 81
When God finished making the world 302
When I feel blue 263
When I feel small and quite alone 264
When I lie down, I go to sleep 350
When I'm frightened of the dark 365
When I put my hands together 364
When it rains in summer 28
When I travel in a bus I see 59
When in the night I sleepless lie 339
When we go out my dad says 169
Wide as the world 53
You made the people that I meet 205

The publisher has made every effort to check that all material included in this publication is in the public domain. If any inadvertent breach of copyright has been made, we will be pleased to rectify any omission in future editions.

THE SOUL OF A NEW CUISINE

088

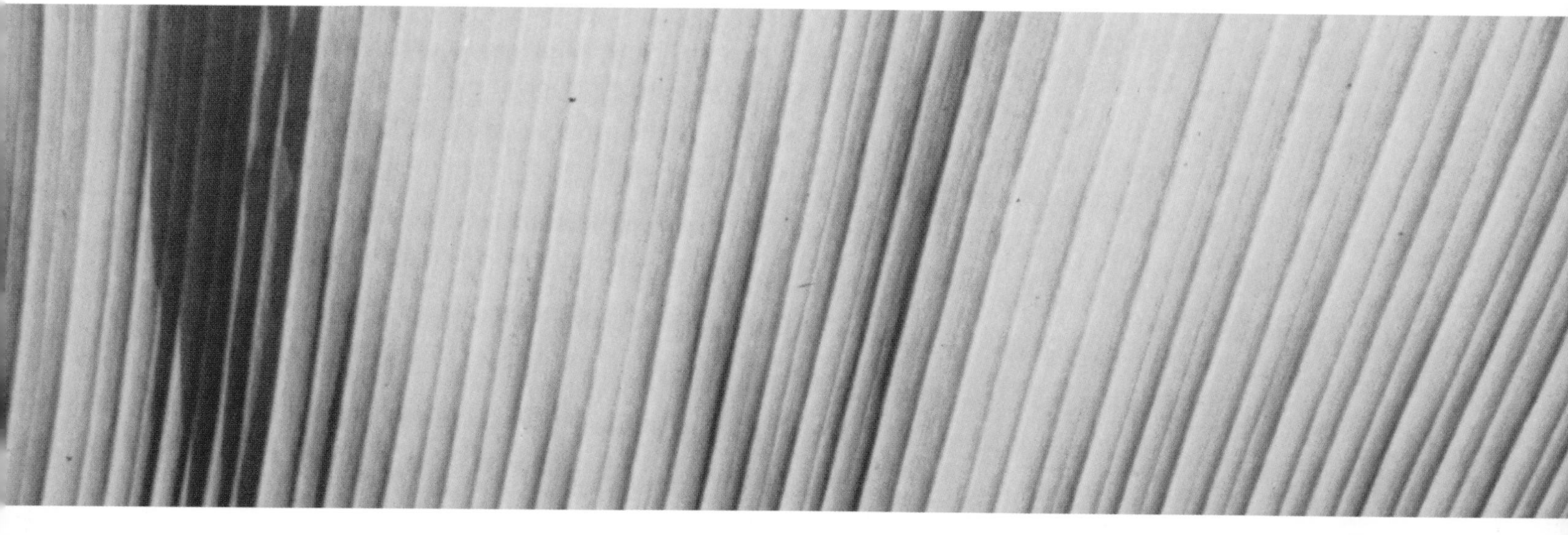

THE SOUL OF A NEW CUISINE

A DISCOVERY OF THE FOODS AND FLAVORS OF AFRICA

MARCUS SAMUELSSON

WITH HEIDI SACKO WALTERS

PHOTOGRAPHS BY GEDIYON KIFLE

FOREWORD BY DESMOND TUTU

WILEY

John Wiley & Sons, Inc.

This book is printed on acid-free paper. ∞

Published by John Wiley & Sons, Inc., Hoboken, New Jersey
Published simultaneously in Canada

For general information about our other products and services, please contact our Customer Care Department within the United States at (800) 762-2974, outside the United States at (317) 572-3993 or fax (317) 572-4002.
Wiley also publishes its books in a variety of electronic formats. Some content that appears in print may not be available in electronic books.
For more information about Wiley products, visit our web site at www.wiley.com.

LIBRARY OF CONGRESS CATALOGING-IN-PUBLICATION DATA:
Samuelsson, Marcus.
The soul of a new cuisine : a discovery of the foods and flavors of Africa / Marcus Samuelsson.
p. cm.
Includes bibliographical references and index.
ISBN-13: 978-0-7645-6911-1 (cloth)
ISBN-10: 0-7645-6911-2 (cloth)
1. Cookery, African. I. Title.
TX725.A4S26 2006
641.596–dc22
2005028312

Printed in China
10 9 8 7 6 5 4 3 2

TO MY SISTER LINDA FANTAYE, for looking out for your little brother. Thank you for never giving up on the search for our family ties.

—MARCUS KASSAHUN

CONTENTS

FOREWORD ix

PREFACE xi

ACKNOWLEDGMENTS xv

INTRODUCTION xvii

INGREDIENTS AND EQUIPMENT 1

SPICE BLENDS AND RUBS 8

CONDIMENTS, SAUCES, AND DIPS 38

SALADS AND SIDES 74

SOUPS AND STEWS 108

BREADS, DUMPLINGS, AND SANDWICHES 136

VEGETABLES 168

FISH AND SEAFOOD 198

POULTRY 238

MEAT 266

DESSERTS AND DRINKS 298

SOURCES 336

INDEX 337

FOREWORD

When I think of Africa and its cuisine, the creation story comes to mind. Most of us are familiar with the first few chapters of Genesis in the Bible. Isn't there a veritable explosion of creativity? God, it could be said, went on a real spree, almost, one might say, an orgy of creativity—where there was chaos, darkness, and disorder, now there was order, cosmos, and light, and what a kaleidoscope of diversity. There were trees, stars, a sun and moon, rivers and seas, fish, fowl, and birds and animals, not just one sort but a whole range of different animals; giraffes, elephants, lions, tigers, sheep, and we could go on and on, and then there was Adam. He was all by himself and God saw that it was not good for man to be alone. And then we have that lovely story of how Eve came about.

We say in Africa that a person is a person through other persons. A solitary human being is a contradiction in terms. We are made for togetherness, for friendship, for fellowship. Food is a part of that fellowship. We are created to live in a delicate network of interdependence and we are different precisely in order to know our need of one another. Diversity, difference is the essence of who we are. Nowhere is that diversity and sense of fellowship more apparent than on the continent of Africa, as expressed through its many varied cuisines and tradition of hospitality.

I come from South Africa, a beautiful land richly endowed by God with wonderful natural resources, wide expanses, rolling mountains, singing birds, bright shining stars out of blue skies, with radiant sunshine, golden sunshine. This land, which carried the opprobrium of the world for its vicious apartheid policy, is home to a vast array of people and thus cuisines. The land here is fertile and bears everything from the grapes that make the famed wine—pinotage—to the corn that is the base to mealie pap, to the spices that comprise Indian and Cape Malay cuisine. I mention South Africa because it is the land I know best and because it is a microcosm of the world and an example of what is to be found in other lands in differing degrees; a fantastic array of remarkable difference and diversity, different languages, different cultures, different ethnicities, different this, different that. We are indeed the rainbow people of God.

I commend Marcus for recognizing the culinary gifts that Africa offers and for undertaking the huge and important task of documenting its cuisine and sharing it with the world so that people everywhere can experience the cuisine and hospitality of this stunning continent and its rainbow nations. His work pays homage to Africa's humanity. Let us break bread together and celebrate our diversity.

Archbishop Desmond Tutu

INTRODUCTION

TO UNDERSTAND AFRICAN COOKING, YOU HAVE TO UNDERSTAND AFRICA. But understanding this enormous continent is no easy task. People often speak about Africa as if the entire continent were one homogeneous place. Nothing could be further from the truth, for Africa is a land of contrasts, stretching from the arid deserts of the Sahara, to the lush, tropical rain forests of the Congo, to the verdant, fertile farmlands of South Africa. It is the second largest continent on the planet, covering nearly 12 million square miles, with more than fifty-five countries.

It's a land of diversity, where more than eight hundred languages and dialects are spoken and every major religion is practiced. It's also a land of turbulence, with ever-shifting borders and governments. Throughout its thousands of years of history, Africa has been explored and exploited by foreign powers, and the colonization and near constant warfare the continent has endured has left much of it impoverished with an ever-evolving culture. The result is a continent with rich and varied societies and a distinctive array of arts, crafts, music, traditions, and celebrations, all of which make each region and country unique and special.

This uniqueness extends to the foods of the continent as well. Africa's place in history as a land of conquest has resulted in cuisines based on simple preparations that make the most of what is available. Most of the cooking is what we think of as "poor man's food": simple stews, grilled meats and fish, steamed vegetables, filling side dishes, and a range of breads. Yet these simple foods are anything but dull. African cooks coax flavor from every piece of meat, fish, poultry, or vegetable, and no scrap is wasted. Chilies and spices are used generously to enliven dishes with an often unexpected vibrance. Ingredients range from those native to the continent—fava beans, black-eyed peas, okra, sesame seeds, yams—to the spices, limes, oranges, tomatoes, peppers, and corn introduced by explorers, traders, and settlers from Europe, the Middle East, India, and the rest of Asia.

Hospitality is a hallmark of the continent, with meals as the gathering time for friends and families. Throughout many parts of Africa, traditional meals are served around a large table, with a communal platter in the center. A jug or dish of water is passed around, so guests can wash their hands before dipping into the starches, soups, and stews that make up a typical meal. In places such as Mali, Nigeria, Eritrea, and Somalia, fingers are used in place of knife and fork to scoop up bites of the various meats and stews, and it's considered a sign of politeness to leave a little food on the plate to indicate you've had enough to eat.

To write about Africa is to accept that in a continent so vast, you can never experience it all, or convey all the wonders it holds. I've grouped African cuisine into four geographic regions—North, West, East, and Southern—by identifying similar techniques, ingredients, and approaches that are used throughout the areas. But in truth this vastly oversimplifies the richness of the variety that can be found not just from country to country but from village to village. In this book, I focus on the countries I've seen and experi-

enced, and so I am certain I'm omitting much of the rich and beautiful culture of the countries I have yet to explore. Following, I give an overview of each region and the cooking styles that loosely connect the countries within each region.

NORTH AFRICA

Perhaps the Africa that's most familiar outside of the continent is the Africa of the Maghreb, the region including the countries of Morocco, Algeria, Tunisia, Sudan, and Libya. This colorful land of mystery is a place of fascination to most Westerners, and with good reason. Located just a short boat ride across the Mediterranean from Europe, it nevertheless feels like a world away, with a completely foreign vibe that is as shocking as it is exciting.

In Arabic, "Maghreb" means "where the sun sets"—a reference to the region's location as the westernmost part of the Arab world. The name is apt because Islamic culture defines the region. Mosques and mazes of medinas dominate city landscapes and no end of bizarre experiences can be found in the bazaars, where carpets, spices, teas, trinkets, and more can be found. It's a land saturated in color—the red earth tones of the desert, the jewel tones of tiled buildings, and great swathes of green landscape.

North Africa encompasses a varied climate, stretching from the tropical coastal regions, to the frigid tips of the Atlas Mountains, to the parched edges of the great Sahara. Years of French, Spanish, and German occupation left very little impact on the region. The food, with a harmonious blend of floral spices, bears little resemblance to either European or sub-Saharan African cuisine. Lamb is the dominant meat, and couscous and tagines are the immediately recognizable foods.

Although it borders the Maghreb, Egypt's culture, traditions, and food have more in common with the Middle East than with its immediate neighbors. When most people think of Egypt, romantic images of the Sphinx, pyramids, pharaohs, and mummies come to mind, but this country's modern-day life is just as intriguing as its ancient history. The streets of Cairo are alive with merchants and shoppers, and modern-day skyscrapers and condominium towers are just minutes from the majestic ancient marvels, which have been attracting tourists since the days of the ancient Greeks and Romans. The Nile River is the country's lifeline, bringing fertility to the Nile Valley and Delta as it flows from the Sudanese border to the Mediterranean Sea. It's easy to see why the ancient peoples worshipped the river and the life it gave. Although the days of paganism are long past, religion still plays a large part in day-to-day life in Egypt, where Islam, Judaism, and Christianity coexist. Pigeon, broad beans, falafel, spiced breads, and hard-boiled eggs are just a few of the foods with ancient roots in Egyptian cooking, and it's worth noting that culinarily a huge debt is owed to the ancient Egyptians, who created beer, bread, and foie gras—three things found all over the world today.

WEST AFRICA

Defining West Africa is a daunting task. This vast region, nearly as large as the continental United States, comprises seventeen countries—Mauritania, Senegal, the Gambia, Guinea, Guinea-Bissau, Sierra Leone, Liberia, Côte d'Ivoire, Mali, Burkina Faso, Ghana, Togo, Benin, Niger, Nigeria, Cameroon, and Cape Verde—that share similar geography, history, and traditions, but are still home to countless differences. Within this region, I include five more countries that are not typically categorized as West Africa geographically, but which share a common culinary bond with the region—Chad, Central African Republic, Equatorial Guinea, Gabon, and São Tomé and Principe.

Except for the very northern reaches, which occupy the southern fringes of the Sahara, most of West Africa is tropical savanna as far as the eye can see. In this sweltering climate, old-time hospitality is a given and strangers are greeted with a warm welcome and handshake. No home is entered without the offer of food and drink, and all day long women are at work preparing meals that range from small gatherings to grand feasts. These foods tend to be humble, with the emphasis on starch served with a stew or soup made with fish, chicken, or such bush meats as cane rat, gazelle, or monkey. Chilies are present in many dishes, especially in southern Nigeria, where the food is blisteringly hot.

Traveling through the region is a dizzying juxtaposition of old and new. The cities are crammed with cars, people chatting on cell phones, and every other modern convenience, while in the rural farm areas people perform tasks just as they might have hundreds of years ago. Food is still cooked outside in pots set over a three-stone fire, and meats and fish are wrapped in banana leaves and set in the ashes to steam. A common early morning scene in one of West Africa's remote villages is that of two young women with perfect posture facing each other over a giant mortar and pestle as they share the task of pounding groundnuts (what we know as peanuts) to make mafé, the famed groundnut stew of the region. Later in the day, the silhouettes of men scaling the skinny trunks of palm trees to retrieve bottles filled with fresh palm wine can be seen throughout the flat countryside.

This ancient land has a far-reaching history of tribal kingdoms and empires, but apart from Liberia, which was established in the 1840s by the United States as a home for freed slaves, today's West African countries are all former colonies of the French, British, or Portuguese. Much of the slave trade was based in West Africa; these slaves carried their culinary traditions with them, introducing native foods such as okra, black-eyed peas, sweet potatoes, watermelon, and sesame seeds to the faraway lands they were taken to.

EAST AFRICA

If you only know Africa from the movies, chances are the landscape of East Africa is what you picture. This stunningly picturesque region—encompassing Eritrea, Somalia, Djibouti, Ethiopia, Kenya, Tanzania, Uganda, Rwanda, Burundi, Congo, Malawi, and Zambia—is home to a dramatic landscape of seemingly endless savannas, the sparkling blue waters of Lake Victoria, tropical rain forests, the history-rich Red Sea, and the peaks of the mythical Mount Kilimanjaro. Lions, gazelles, zebras, ostriches, monkeys, baboons, gorillas, jackals, mongooses, hyenas, cheetahs, elephants, rhinos, warthogs, hippos, and more roam this dramatic natural wonderland, and the acres of parkland that have been set aside as preserves attract thousands of visitors on safari each year.

The Great Rift Valley that runs through much of the region is known as the cradle of humanity because human life is thought to have originated here. Perhaps it is because it is where mankind began that East Africa attracts people from all over the world, beginning at least as early as 700 A.D., when Arabs from the Arabian Peninsula and Persia settled to establish trading posts along the Indian Ocean, eventually intermarrying with native Africans to create the Swahili culture that now dominates the region. The Arabs brought their spices and cooking techniques with them, but it was later settlements by Indian traders that left the most indelible mark on the cuisine of the region, as they introduced their curries, spice blends, and breads to the foods of the region.

As in the rest of Africa, starch is the staple of the diet, stretched with a small amount of soup or stew for flavor. Ugali, a thick, bland porridge made from cornmeal or millet flour, is the most common staple and a favorite of many of the people I met. Fish and shellfish, both fresh and dried, are abundant along the coastal saltwater areas and inland lakes and rivers. Cattle are commonly considered a sign of wealth, not food, particularly by the legendary Masai herdsmen who live off the milk and blood of their herds.

Although it is geographically part of East Africa, my homeland of Ethiopia bears little resemblance to its surrounding area and deserves special mention. The only country in Africa never colonized by a foreign power, Ethiopia has a remarkably intact culture and a completely distinctive cuisine based on injera (a spongy, crepelike sourdough bread made from a grain called teff) and a variety of meat, fish, poultry, and vegetarian stews.

SOUTHERN AFRICA

Of all the places I visited in Africa, perhaps the one I most anticipated seeing was South Africa's Cape Town. My friend Jessica Harris, a noted African food historian, once referred to Cape Town as the Cape of Good Cooks because of the well-deserved reputation Cape Malay cooks have earned for their artful blending of Malaysian, Indian, European, and Afrikaner cooking. Originally brought to South Africa as slaves for the Dutch farmer colonists known as the Boers, the Cape Malays forged their own culture, creating a distinct set of traditions, customs, and foods that soon spread into the black and Afrikaner worlds. Their beautifully balanced bredies (spiced mutton with vegetables), sosaties (spiced mutton or lamb skewers with apricots), koesisters (spiced doughnuts), and other wonderful dishes dazzled, delighted, and inspired me.

But Southern Africa is more than just Cape Malay culture. Homo sapiens have been ranging the stunning landscapes of South Africa, Botswana, Zimbabwe, Lesotho, Swaziland, and Namibia for more than fifty thousand years, and the many tribes of the region have developed their own distinctive cultures. It is one of the most beautiful areas of the world, featuring the best of what Africa has to offer—generous natural resources, sparkling gems, the awe-inspiring Victoria Falls, the vast Kalahari Desert, enormous game parks, stunning cities, turquoise waters, and ancient ruins that date back to the earliest days of man.

Beyond the coast, Southern Africa's island nations offer a different perspective, with a glorious fusion of influences from around the world combined in a uniquely African way. There's no other country like Madagascar, the fourth largest island on Earth—its emerald forests and shimmering streams are home to animals and plants found nowhere else on the planet, including rare lemurs, birds, and frogs that attract visitors from around the world. Culinarily, Madagascar is on the map for the fine vanilla and coffee that Malagasy farmers produce. The breathtaking landscape of Comoros, an island nation off the coast of Madagascar, ranges from steep mountains to low hills, while the more politically stable islands of

Seychelles and Mauritius attract tourists with their friendly people, azure waters, and white beaches.

To the north, Angola and Mozambique, on opposite coasts of the continent, were once sister colonies of Portugal and to this day maintain a distinct similarity in their culture and in their food. Portuguese traders introduced corn, beans, chili peppers, and more from their colonies in the New World, and these foods were swiftly incorporated into the native diet.

WHEN I BEGAN TRAVELING THROUGH THIS INCREDIBLY DIVERSE LAND, I went with preconceptions about the food I would find. But Africa never stopped surprising me and by the time I left, those preconceptions had all broken down. The continent is so huge and home to so many people from all over the world that there are no "rules"—as soon as you think "no one does this here," you'll find someone who does. It made writing about the foods of the entire continent a challenge.

As I was working on this project, a number of people said to me, "Africa is so huge and so diverse. How can you possibly write a cookbook about the whole continent?" I understand their question, and from the start had a clear idea that this book would not be a definitive encyclopedia of African cooking. Rather, this cookbook is a reflection of the Africa I've seen, experienced, and appreciated. It's a very personal voyage that highlights my own interpretation of Africa and its cuisines, and it provides just an overview of the foods of this vast area, giving you a taste of what the continent has to offer. I feature traditional recipes for dishes that have been handed down through generations, but I've also created my own interpretations of dishes that take the African tastes and techniques I've grown to love as a jumping-off point to create my own African-inspired cuisine, just as other chefs over the last twenty or thirty years have introduced the wonderful flavors of Italian, Asian, and Latin cooking. As more and more people travel to the continent and African ingredients become increasingly available, it's a cuisine whose time has come, and my goal with this book is to help you bring your own dream of Africa into your home kitchen.

Algiers
Tunis
Oran
Rabat
Casablanca
MOROCCO
Atlas Mountains
TUNISIA
Tripoli
Benghazi
Alexandria
Cairo
Laayoun
ALGERIA
Ghadâmes
LIBYA
Western Desert
Nile
Dakhla
Western Sahara
Marzuq
Libyan Desert
EGYPT
F'Dérik
Ahaggar
Mt. Tahat
Aswan
Nouakchott
MAURITANIA
Sahara Desert
Tibesti
MALI
Nubian Desert
Port Sudan
Tombouctou
A F R I C A
Atbara
Dakar
SENEGAL
Niger
NIGER
CHAD
Khartoum
Asmara
GAMBIA
Bamako
Niamey
SUDAN
ERITREA
GUINEA BISSAU
BURKINA FASO
Ndjamena
Jebel Marra
El Obeid
GUINEA
BENIN
Conakry
NIGERIA
SIERRA LEONE
GHANA
Abuja
Berbera
Freetown
IVORY COAST
TOGO
Ibadan
CAMEROON
Addis Ababa
SOMALIA
CENTRAL AFRICAN REPUBLIC
Ethiopian Highlands
Monrovia
ETHIOPIA
LIBERIA
Abidjan
Accra
Lome
Porto Novo
Bangui
Yaoundé
Margherita Peak
UGANDA
KENYA
Mogadishu
Libreville
Mbandaka
Kampala
Kirinyaga
GABON
DEMOCRATIC REPUBLIC OF THE CONGO
RWANDA
Nairobi
Kismayu
CONGO
Brazzaville
Kigali
Lake Victoria
Kilimanjaro
Kinshasa
Mombasa
Matadi
Kananga
Zanzibar
TANZANIA
Dar-es-Salaam
Luanda
Angola Plateau
Likasi
Lobito
ANGOLA
MALAWI
MOZAMBIQUE
Huambo
Ndola
Antisiranana
Lilongwe
Namibe
ZAMBIA
Lusaka
Livingstone
Harare
MADAGASCAR
Okavango Delta
ZIMBABWE
Beira
NAMIBIA
Antananarivo
Namib Desert
Windhoek
BOTSWANA
Gaborone
Kalahari Desert
Pretoria
Johannesburg
Maputo
Cape Ste. Marie
SOUTH AFRICA
Maseru
LESOTHO
Drakensberg
Durban
Cape Town
Great Karoo
Port Elizabeth
Cape of Good Hope

INGREDIENTS AND EQUIPMENT

PANTRY

The African kitchen is not as foreign as you may expect—many of the ingredients used in everyday cooking are found in pantries around the world. There are a number of ingredients, however, that either are unique to Africa or are used in ways that you may not be accustomed to.

Banana Leaves: The wide, striated leaves of the banana tree are frequently used in West Africa to wrap foods for steaming. The leaves are very long, measuring 3 to 4 feet, and should be cut to the needed size. They can be found in Latin, Asian, Caribbean, and African grocery stores and are usually sold frozen.

Beans: Beans are a common source of protein throughout Africa, particularly in countries like Ethiopia, where a large number of religious fast days are observed. I prefer cooking with dried beans rather than using canned beans, which often have a metallic taste. Cover dried beans with cold water and soak for at least 8 hours, or overnight, before cooking them.

Brown Sugar: Brown sugar is manufactured throughout the African continent. My favorite is an organic fair-trade raw-cane demerara from Malawi, which is sold under the Wholesome Sweetners brand at many upscale grocery stores. It has an intense, multifaceted flavor that really stands out in a recipe.

Bulgur: Arab traders introduced many foods to North Africa, including bulgur, a type of cracked wheat. This highly nutritious grain can be found in larger supermarkets, health food stores, and specialty stores, as well as through online sources.

Cardamom: Tanzania is one of the world's largest growers of cardamom, a lovely aromatic spice used to flavor soups, stews, baked goods, and, in Arabic countries, coffee. I suggest buying whole cardamom and grinding it yourself rather than buying preground, as the flavor is much more intense. This is true of all spices, but the flavor difference is especially noticeable for this spice. White and green cardamom pods are available; I prefer white cardamom, which has been bleached, because I think it gives a cleaner, truer taste. Avoid brown or black cardamom, also known as false cardamom, which comes from a different plant. And use cardamom sparingly, as the intense flavor goes a long way.

Cassava: Originally from South America, cassava was brought to Africa by Spanish and Portuguese traders and quickly became a staple food. Probably the most well-known use of the cigar-shaped root is in West Africa, where it is cooked and pounded into a mash called fufu. In addition, the leaves are used as a green vegetable, while the roots are also dried to make cassava meal and tapioca. There are two main types of cassava, bitter and sweet. Cyanide compounds occur naturally in the bitter variety, making it poisonous unless cooked, so only the sweet variety is approved by the USDA for sale in the United States; to be on the safe side, I suggest rinsing any cassava thoroughly before preparing it. Cassava, also known as manioc or yuca, is available in African and Hispanic markets. Look for roots that are firm and even in color and texture.

SPICE BLENDS AND RUBS

Berbere

Awase

Black Olive Oil

Chermoula

Boharat

Dark Spice Mix

Duqqa

Bahama Spice Farm, Tanzania

Ginger Paste

Green Curry Paste

Green Masala

Harissa

Jerk Mix

Ras al-Hanout

Spiced Butter

Yogurt Rub

Za'atar

AT FIRST GLANCE, AFRICAN FOOD SEEMS VERY STRAIGHTFORWARD—meats grilled over an open flame, slow-cooked stews stretched with vegetables and offal, and bland, starchy sides that fill the belly for a full day's work. But my travels throughout the continent put an end to this assumption—as I ate my way through Africa, in country after country I found the cooking to be startlingly flavorful and full of surprises.

You can't begin to think about African cooking without first understanding the importance of spice blends, which are used to elevate simple cooking techniques to an excitingly varied and intensive level. Just as European cooking relies on salt to give dimension to dishes, cooks throughout Africa use spice blends and rubs to season their meats, poultry, fish, and other seafood before and after cooking. With blends that vary from region to region—ranging from sweet to spicy with varying degrees of heat, and featuring everything from hot chili peppers or peppermint leaves to sesame seeds and ginger—it's an exciting and flavor-packed way to eat that awed me at first bite.

From the start, I loved the searing heat of Ethiopian stews, the delicate nuances of Moroccan tagines, the relentlessly spicy peanut stews of West Africa, and the coconut- and spice-infused richness of the Cape Malay cuisine of South Africa. But what surprised me the most was how hauntingly familiar many of the dishes seemed—in them I tasted ginger, cinnamon, saffron, cloves, nutmeg, cumin, curries . . . tastes I associated with Asia and Europe, South America and India. How, I wondered, had Africa come to be the melting pot for all these flavors?

The reason, I learned, is that Africa played a major but little-known role in the spice trade, as invaders, settlers, and travelers crisscrossed the continent for centuries, introducing spices and ingredients from around the world. In Egypt, routes for the trade of eastern spices, oils, and fragrances were established very early on: nearly five thousand years ago, spice markets near Giza provided the builders of Egypt's great pyramids with spices to "improve their strength," and ancient Egyptians used spices for embalming, as perfume, and to fumigate their homes. In the seventh century, Arab invaders settled in northern and eastern Africa, bringing with them spices that were quickly incorporated into the local cooking. Berber traders carried these spices into West Africa, and from there into the interior. Elsewhere in Africa, spices of other lands became an important part of local cooking—Indian settlers on the eastern coast brought their curries, and South Africa's Malay slaves introduced the spices that are so prominent a part of South African cooking today. The result is a continent of cuisines that offer a delicious flavor journey around the globe, with an exceptional balance of layered tastes and flavors that sparkle on the palate. It's fusion cuisine at its most elegant and organic—and most successful—and it all stems from the spice blends developed hundreds of years ago.

In this chapter, I've compiled my favorite blends, representing the best of each region. And don't forget that these blends provide an easy way to introduce the flavors of Africa to your everyday cooking. If you don't have the time or inclination to make one of the recipes from this book but want to add a taste of Africa to your meal, just use the blend of your choice—for instance, rubbing delicately flavored ras al-hanout over a chicken breast or fiery piri piri sauce on a bass fillet next time you fire up the grill.

Because the freshness of spices has such an impact on their intensity, African cooks typically don't measure exact quantities, instead relying on their sense of taste and smell to strike the right balance. I've given measurements, but feel free to modify them, adding a little more of this and a little less of that according to your personal preference. For the most flavorful results, keep in mind that I recommend using whole spices and grinding them by hand in a mortar and pestle. In a pinch, ground spices will work, but you'll lose some of the intensity and flavor.

BERBERE

For me, Ethiopian cooking is built on three building blocks: injera, the local bread that is served with each meal; nit'ir qibe, a spiced butter that provides a rich base; and berbere, a complex blend of chili peppers and spices that gives the cuisine its signature rich, layered flavors.

In Ethiopia, the preparation of berbere takes days—chilies are dried in the sun for three days, then ground in a mortar and pestle, mixed with ground spices, and set in the sun to dry again—and it is usually made in huge amounts, using as many as fifteen pounds of chilies and five pounds of garlic. I've streamlined the recipe and cut the yield drastically for a simplified preparation that maintains the integrity of flavors but takes only fifteen minutes to make.

Each Ethiopian family has its own recipe for this universal seasoning, with varying degrees of heat and spiciness. Traditionally, berbere is used to flavor Ethiopian stews, but I also like to use it as a rub for beef and lamb.

1 teaspoon fenugreek seeds
½ cup ground dried serrano chilies or other ground dried chilies
½ cup paprika
2 tablespoons salt
2 teaspoons ground ginger
2 teaspoons onion powder
1 teaspoon ground cardamom, preferably freshly ground
1 teaspoon ground nutmeg
½ teaspoon garlic powder
¼ teaspoon ground cloves
¼ teaspoon ground cinnamon
¼ teaspoon ground allspice

Finely grind the fenugreek seeds with a mortar and pestle or in an electric spice or coffee grinder. Stir together with the remaining ingredients in a small bowl until well combined.

Store in an airtight container in the refrigerator for up to 3 months.

MAKES 1 CUP

AWASE

Berbere, the dried chili-based spice blend, is the cornerstone of almost all Ethiopian dishes. But even berbere can't fuel enough fire for heat-seeking Ethiopian palates. Awase, a blisteringly hot condiment made with berbere, is used as an Ethiopian-style ketchup, served on the side to up the heat quotient of stews and soups. Use it sparingly to add heat to any dish.

2 tablespoons Berbere (page 12) **or mild chili powder**
1 teaspoon cayenne pepper
½ teaspoon ground ginger
¼ teaspoon ground cardamom, preferably freshly ground
½ teaspoon salt
2 tablespoons fresh lemon juice
1 tablespoon dry red wine
1 tablespoon water

Combine the berbere, cayenne, ginger, cardamom, and salt in a small sauté pan and toast over medium heat, stirring constantly, until fragrant, about 30 seconds.

Remove the pan from the heat. Whisk in the lemon juice, red wine, and water. Let cool.

Store in an airtight container in the refrigerator for up to 1 week.

MAKES ABOUT ¼ CUP

BLACK OLIVE OIL

When considering the cooking of the Mediterranean, many people look only to the north and completely overlook the countries that border the southern side of the sea. But in fact, North African cooking—especially in Morocco and Tunisia—shares many similarities with the culinary traditions of Spain, Italy, and Greece, particularly the reliance on olives, which are served at the start of every meal, and olive oils. This black olive oil is inspired by the cooking of North Africa and is great to use as a rub for lamb or fish, or even as a dressing for salad.

½ cup black olives, pitted
2 anchovy fillets, minced, or 1½ teaspoons anchovy paste
2 cups extra virgin olive oil
2 garlic cloves
2 thyme sprigs, leaves only, chopped

Combine all the ingredients in a blender and puree until smooth.

Store tightly covered in the refrigerator for up to 1 week.

MAKES 2½ CUPS

CHERMOULA

I think chermoula is a perfect representation of the best of North African culinary traditions—it's rich and varied in flavor, with underlying spiciness so you can really taste all the distinct spices. Cooks all over northern Africa use chermoula, particularly in Morocco and Tunisia, where it is typically used as a rub for fish. I like to toss it with chicken or meat when I'm grilling to add a bright and lively note of herbs and citrus with just a hint of heat.

8 garlic cloves
½ cup small parsley sprigs
⅓ cup small cilantro sprigs
Grated zest of 2 lemons
4 teaspoons paprika
2 teaspoons chili powder
2 teaspoons ground cumin
1 cup olive oil

Combine the garlic, parsley, cilantro, lemon zest, paprika, chili powder, and cumin in a blender and blend on low speed to a coarse puree; don't process until smooth. With the blender running, add the oil in a thin, steady stream and blend until a thick paste forms.

Store in a tightly covered container in the refrigerator for up to 2 weeks.

MAKES 1½ CUPS

BOHARAT

One of the highlights of my job is that I meet people from all around the world, giving me an international experience every day. When I first became interested in African cooking, one of the cooks who works with me shared his family recipe for boharat, an incredibly distinctive and aromatic spice blend that is the cornerstone of many North African and Middle Eastern dishes. To me, this lovely blend showcases the Arabic influences that prevail throughout North Africa—rose petal lends a floral note and lemon powder gives a bright, citrus component, while the remaining spices highlight the variety of flavors that made their way through Morocco's legendary spice trade. Look for rose petals and lemon powder in Middle Eastern markets or specialty spice shops.

¼ cup ground allspice
1 tablespoon freshly ground black pepper
1 tablespoon ground cinnamon
1 tablespoon ground nutmeg
1 teaspoon ground cardamom, preferably freshly ground
1 teaspoon ground cloves
1 teaspoon ground ginger
1 teaspoon dried rose petals
1 teaspoon dried lemon powder

Stir together all the ingredients in a small bowl until well combined.

Store tightly covered in the refrigerator for up to 2 weeks.

MAKES ½ CUP

DARK SPICE MIX

I was trained in European-style cooking, where salt and pepper balance the flavors of individual dishes. African cooking takes a completely different approach, relying on spice blends to give dishes a sense of equilibrium, much as curries do in Indian cookery. This paste combines spices used all over the continent for beautiful layers of flavor that lend an exotic kick to poultry or meat.

1 tablespoon cumin seeds
1½ teaspoons poppy seeds
One 3-inch piece ginger, peeled and grated
2 teaspoons mustard seeds
2 teaspoons fennel seeds
6 cloves
1 teaspoon cardamom pods
1 teaspoon black peppercorns
2 cinnamon sticks, crushed into small pieces
2 Scotch bonnet chilies, seeds and ribs removed, chopped
½ cup peanut oil

Heat a small sauté pan over low heat. Add the cumin seeds, poppy seeds, ginger, mustard seeds, fennel seeds, cloves, cardamom, peppercorns, cinnamon sticks, and chilies and toast until fragrant, stirring occasionally, about 30 seconds.

Transfer to a blender and puree. With the blender running, add the oil in a thin, steady stream and blend to a coarse puree.

Store in an airtight container in the refrigerator for up to 3 weeks.

MAKES ABOUT 1 CUP

DUQQA

The word "duqqa" is derived from the Arabic word meaning "to pound," and with good reason, because the nuts and spices are crushed together with a mortar and pestle for a richly textured result. Originally developed in the Middle East, this lovely spice blend has made its way throughout northern Africa. It's especially popular in Egypt, where it is eaten with bread dipped in olive oil at breakfast or as a snack. Recipes for duqqa vary from family to family, with mint as the signature flavor. While you can find prepared duqqa in some Middle Eastern markets, it's so easy to make and the fresh preparation is so superior in flavor and aroma that I recommend only using homemade. Do not try making this in a blender, as the sesame seeds will turn to a paste.

2 tablespoons hulled pumpkin seeds
2 tablespoons peanuts
1 teaspoon black peppercorns
2 teaspoons sesame seeds
8 mint leaves
4 thyme sprigs, leaves only
1 teaspoon coriander seeds
1 teaspoon cumin seeds
1½ teaspoons salt

Heat a small sauté pan over medium heat. Add the pumpkin seeds, peanuts, and peppercorns and toast, stirring, until fragrant, about 5 minutes. Add the sesame seeds, mint leaves, thyme leaves, coriander, and cumin and toast, stirring frequently, until fragrant, about 5 minutes.

Transfer to a mortar and grind with the pestle, or grind in an electric spice or coffee grinder until the seeds and nuts are coarsely crushed. Add the salt.

Store in a tightly covered container in the refrigerator for up to 10 days.

MAKES ½ CUP

I was in Zanzibar, and it felt like being in paradise.

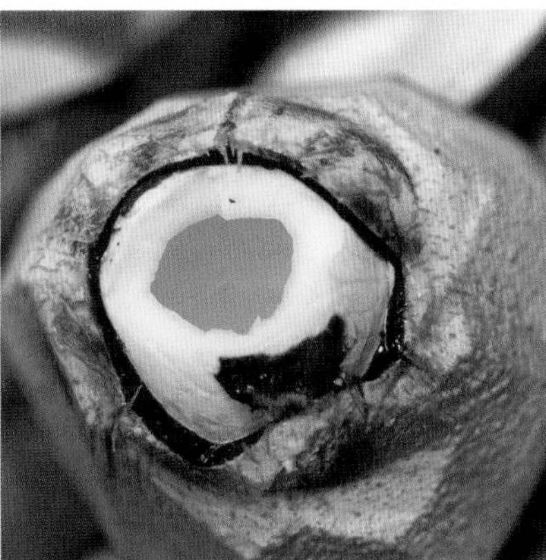

I WAS VISITING THE BAHAMA SPICE FARM, a small, private farm where the faint, musky smell of cloves and cardamom danced on the breeze. Before me stretched a riotous tangle of greenery, sprouting spices I never imagined I'd have the opportunity to see growing—much less all in one place. As a chef, seeing how the spices I use daily are cultivated was like being in my own personal garden of Eden. It was an awe-inspiring afternoon I will never forget.

A guide walked me through the farm, challenging me to recognize the different spices that grew before us. Handing me a leaf from a large tree, he urged me to smell it to see if I could recognize the aroma. I sniffed and ventured a guess—"Cinnamon?"—and he smiled, happy to have stumped me. "No, it's nutmeg," he said, cracking open the mottled yellow fruit to reveal the tough brown kernel of nutmeg at its center.

And so it went on our journey along the rambling path that ran through the spice patches. Before me, vanilla beans, ginger, cardamom, cloves, lemongrass, cocoa, cinnamon—all the magical flavors that inspire me every day—sprang from the ground, seemingly at random: a nutmeg tree here, a vanilla-bean vine there, a cinnamon tree in the distance. We pulled ginger roots and lemongrass stalks from the ground, and watched our guide climb the branches of a tree to pluck a blossom that yielded tender, plump pink cloves, which would later be dried until they were shriveled and brown.

At the end of the tour, one of the boys accompanying us twisted a length of rope into a figure 8, hooked his feet into it, and used it to help him shimmy up the trunk of a tall, graceful coconut tree, disappearing into the sky to send a storm of coconuts raining down on us. Back on the ground, he cracked open a coconut and handed it to me. As I sipped the fresh, warm juice, I remembered hearing that long-ago sailors passing Zanzibar used to claim they could smell the scent of cloves drifting from the island far out to sea. Today, Zanzibari farmers still eke out a living growing spices on small plots of land, but there was a time when spice plantations brought great riches to Zanzibar, a time whose legacy can still be seen in Stone Town, the faded but opulent heart of this vibrant island.

Stone Town is one of the most magical cities I've ever visited. It's a city of surprises—twisting narrow streets that seem to lead to nowhere, grand Arab palaces, Persian baths, mosques, temples, churches, hotels, restaurants, and shops, and sudden glimpses of the Indian Ocean framed between the crumbling stone buildings.

This magical, mysterious town is the place where the African, Arab, and Indian worlds meet. Hundreds of years ago, African fishermen, Arab and Persian traders, and Indian merchants all settled on the island. The Portuguese occupied Zanzibar beginning in 1503, but were forced out by the Omani Arabs in the late 1600s. Their defeat was followed by more than two hundred years of rule by Arab sultans.

The sultans transformed Zanzibar, introducing cloves from Madagascar and building the first spice plantations. Thanks to the spice trade, the island quickly grew rich and the newly wealthy townspeople began rebuilding their mud homes with stone. The traditional Islamic modesty of these homes was accented with beautifully carved and studded doors, which are now one of the hallmarks of Stone Town. I was told these

doors served a dual purpose—their ornate carving was a way for wealthy homeowners to show off their riches, while the studs were a symbol of protection for the inhabitants.

But, as in many of the places I visited in Africa, you can't ignore history. All this grandeur has a dark side: at the height of the slave trade, as many as sixty thousand slaves a year were transported from the mainland to Zanzibar and sold to owners in Arabia, India, and French Indian Ocean possessions. I visited one of the prisons where the slaves were held—a cramped, dark, stark contrast to the stunning palaces built by the sultans who grew rich from the sale of slaves and spices.

During my brief visit, I drank in the sights, smells, and sounds of Zanzibar: fishermen sailing off in elegant dhows as the sun set over the Indian Ocean, the scent of grilled fish wafting from Stone Town's nightly waterfront market at Forodhani Gardens, and the calling of the muezzin—the crier who summons the Muslim faithful to prayer five times a day—from the mosque near our hotel. It's a place of magic and mystique, whose very name conjures up a sense of enchantment and the smell of spices.

ZA'ATAR

Za'atar is one of my favorites of North Africa's many spice blends. Delicate and fragrant, it has a distinctive citrusy flavor from the sumac and a rich texture that makes it an excellent rub for fish, poultry, or meats, or to add bright flavor to soups and stews. I also like to mix three parts za'atar with one part olive oil for a delicious dip for bread.

2 tablespoons sesame seeds
1 tablespoon dried thyme
1 tablespoon dried oregano
2 tablespoons ground sumac (see page 5)
1 teaspoon salt

Toast the sesame seeds in a small sauté pan over low heat until golden brown, about 1½ minutes. Remove from the heat and set aside to cool.

Mix together the thyme, oregano, and sumac in a small bowl, then stir in the sesame seeds and salt.

Store in a tightly sealed container in a cool, dark place for up to 2 weeks.

MAKES ⅓ CUP

Chickpea-Eggplant Dip

Barbecue Sauce

Chili Mayonnaise

Beet-Ginger Chutney

Plantain Chutney

Quince Chutney

Fresh Cheese with Chives

Papaya Ketchup

Pickled Green and Yellow Papayas

Pickled Onions

Piri Piri

Pistachio Rouille

Preserved Citrus Peel

CONDIMENTS, SAUCES, AND DIPS

Rum-Pickled Chilies

Sakay

J'mal Fna, Marrakech, Morocco

Mango Sambal

Almond Sambal

Cucumber Sambal

Tamarind Vinaigrette

Tarragon Mustard

Thyme-Roasted Garlic

Tomato Date Jam

Tomato Sauce

White Bean Puree

Yogurt Dip

IT'S HARD TO IMAGINE TUNISIAN FOOD WITHOUT HARISSA, Mozambique cuisine without piri piri sauce, or South Africa's Cape Malay cooking without spicy sambals, because these condiments, sauces, and dips are what make the foods of each region so special and unique. They might seem like an afterthought at first, but if you look closely, there's no escaping that these often simple accompaniments are what informs local foods with the flavors and textures that make them exceptional.

In fact, I've always thought that one of the most telling and interesting ways to learn about a country's cuisine is through its accompaniments—the condiments, relishes, toppings, and spreads that dress up local food. They can also give you a little surprise and help clue you in to a region's history. When I had my first Cape Malay meal in South Africa, the vividly spiced sambals that accompanied my meal were so reminiscent of the flavors of Indonesia and Malaysia that it was no surprise to learn that slaves from that region were brought to the Cape three centuries ago and quickly made their mark on the stodgy Dutch fare of their owners. Likewise, seeing chutneys on the tables of Tanzania immediately let me know that Indian traders and settlers had moved up and down the eastern coast, swirling together the techniques and flavors of the Indian mainland with the ingredients native to these African shores.

As far as my research went, it doesn't hurt that condiments are one of my favorite parts of eating. To me, they're like paints on a canvas, adding a dash of flavor and a daub of freshness to any meal. There's something so refreshing about condiments, which tend to feature the brightest and most distinctive flavors of a region, whether it's the silken and delicate preserved lemons of Morocco—a variation of which is represented here in the Preserved Citrus Peel—the French-influenced Chili Mayonnaise of Senegal, or Trinidad's liquor-infused Rum-Pickled Chilies. All embellish the foods they accompany and give them sophistication, but they tend to be made from inexpensive ingredients people grow in their gardens and have in abundance.

Most of the recipes featured in this chapter will keep for at least a week, so you can build up an incredible pantry of flavorings that can be served together to create an interesting meal on the fly. Try the Tarragon Mustard with a simple grilled chicken breast, spoon the Mango Sambal over a tuna steak, or set out the Tomato Date Jam with a baguette and some Brie the next time you want to add a little excitement to an everyday meal. Whether you're cooking African or not, experiment with serving lots of different accompaniments together and have fun creating a riot of flavors that are new and unexpected.

CHICKPEA-EGGPLANT DIP

Hummus is now so ubiquitous that it's hard to remember it was once an "exotic" food. It was the first Moroccan food I ever had, and since that first bite I've grown to love the simplicity of Morocco's many dips because they're so easy to enjoy. You can serve this hummus-style dip on its own with warm pita wedges, as a spread on sandwiches, or as a distinctive accompaniment to grilled fish or chicken.

2 cups dried chickpeas, soaked in cold water for 8 hours and drained
1 carrot, peeled and cut in half
1 medium Spanish onion, cut in half
4 garlic cloves, peeled
2 eggplants, cut lengthwise in half
¼ cup plus 2 tablespoons olive oil
2 bird's-eye chilies, cut in half, seeds and ribs removed
1 teaspoon Harissa (page 30)
1 teaspoon ground cumin

Combine the chickpeas, carrot, and onion in a medium saucepan, add 4 cups water, and bring to a boil. Reduce the heat and simmer until the chickpeas are very tender, about 1½ hours. Drain, reserving 1 cup of the cooking liquid.

Meanwhile, preheat the oven to 300°F. Toss the garlic and eggplant with ¼ cup of the olive oil and arrange on a roasting pan, eggplant cut side down. Roast for 40 minutes. Add the chilies to the roasting pan, cut side down, and roast for another 10 minutes. Set aside until cool enough to handle.

Scoop the flesh from the eggplant and transfer to a blender. Add the roasted garlic and chilies, chickpeas, harissa, cumin, the remaining 2 tablespoons oil, and 2 to 3 tablespoons of the reserved cooking liquid. Puree, adding more of the cooking liquid 2 to 3 tablespoons at a time as necessary, until the mixture is smooth and creamy.

Serve at room temperature with warm Pita Bread (page 151).

MAKES 3 CUPS

CHUTNEYS Indian traders traveled back and forth between India and the coast of East Africa for centuries, so it's no surprise that their spices and dishes were introduced and took root. Today, chutneys are served up and down the eastern coast, where the Indian practice of cooling down a spicy dish with a sweet relish has taken hold.

BEET-GINGER CHUTNEY

The natural sugars in beets lend a satisfying sweetness to this African-inspired chutney, while the ginger gives a pleasing bite. I like to serve it with the Harissa-Roasted Turkey Breast (page 256) because its lovely flavor and texture are an excellent complement to the bird.

2 tablespoons olive oil
4 shallots, finely chopped
4 garlic cloves, minced
Two 3-inch pieces ginger, peeled and sliced
4 beets, peeled and cut into ½-inch cubes
2 tablespoons honey
4 cardamom pods
2 thyme sprigs
2 tablespoons sugar
1 tablespoon Spiced Butter (page 34) or unsalted butter
2 cups chicken stock
½ teaspoon salt

Heat the oil in a large deep sauté pan over high heat. Add the shallots, garlic, ginger, and beets, reduce the heat to low, and sauté for 10 minutes, stirring occasionally.

Add the honey, cardamom, thyme, sugar, and spiced butter and stir over low heat for 1 minute. Add the chicken stock and bring to a simmer. Reduce the heat and simmer until beets are tender, 45 to 50 minutes.

Remove the cardamom, thyme, and ginger from the chutney and stir in the salt. Let cool.

Store in an airtight container in the refrigerator for up to 2 weeks.

MAKES 2 CUPS

PLANTAIN CHUTNEY

The meaty texture and mild flavor of plantains make them a great canvas for the rainbow of flavors that are highlighted in this untraditional chutney. Try it with lighter dishes like Rice-Crusted Hake (page 219), because it makes the meal fuller and adds sweetness.

¼ cup Spiced Butter (page 34) **or 4 tablespoons (½ stick) unsalted butter**

¼ cup olive oil

2 baking potatoes, peeled and cut into ¾-inch cubes

2 medium white onions, sliced

3 garlic cloves, sliced

One 3-inch piece ginger, peeled and grated

2 tablespoons mustard seeds

2 tablespoons Green Curry Paste (page 26)

1 teaspoon chili powder

1 teaspoon ground cardamom, preferably freshly ground

4 green plantains, peeled (see page 5), **quartered lengthwise, and cut into ¾-inch pieces**

Salt

2 scallions, trimmed and chopped

Melt the butter with the olive oil in a large sauté pan over low heat. Add the potatoes, stirring to coat, and cook, stirring, for 10 to 15 minutes, or until golden brown.

Add the onions, garlic, ginger, mustard seeds, curry paste, chili powder, and cardamom, stir well, and cook until the onions are tender, about 20 minutes.

Add the plantains and cook until they soften, about 10 minutes. Let cool.

Season the chutney with salt. Stir in the scallions before serving.

Store in an airtight container in the refrigerator for up to 3 days.

MAKES 4 CUPS

QUINCE CHUTNEY

Long a favorite in African and Caribbean kitchens, quinces are becoming more and more common here in the United States—and with good reason. It's a firm fruit that holds up well in cooked dishes, and it has a tart apple-and-pear-like flavor that makes it an excellent accompaniment to game (or gamey) meats. If you can't find quinces at your local market, substitute 4 unpeeled ripe plums.

¼ cup olive oil
2 shallots, sliced
1 garlic clove, minced
One 1-inch piece ginger, peeled and grated
1 Scotch bonnet chili, seeds and ribs removed, finely chopped
2 teaspoons mustard seeds
1 teaspoon garam masala
1½ tablespoons brown sugar
1 tablespoon honey
2 quinces, peeled, cored, and cut into 1-inch cubes
1 Granny Smith apple, peeled, cored, and cut into 1-inch cubes
½ cup white wine vinegar
½ cup ruby port
2 thyme sprigs
Grated zest and juice of 1 lime
½ cup raisins
½ teaspoon salt

Heat the olive oil in a large pot over medium heat. Add the shallots, garlic, and ginger and sauté until the shallots are translucent, about 5 minutes. Stir in the chili, mustard seeds, garam masala, brown sugar, and honey and cook, stirring constantly, for 2 minutes.

Add the quinces, apples, vinegar, port, thyme, and lime zest and bring just to a boil. Reduce the heat to low and simmer for 20 minutes.

Remove from the heat and let cool. Remove the thyme sprigs, then fold in the raisins, lime juice, and salt.

Store in a tightly covered container in the refrigerator for up to 2 weeks.

MAKES ABOUT 3 CUPS

FRESH CHEESE WITH CHIVES

Ethiopia's berbere-laden stews are always served with a side of cooling ayib, a tangy, homemade cottage-cheese-like accompaniment. Simple to make, it's wonderful on its own, spread on a piece of injera, or when used to balance the sharpness of heavily spiced foods.

2 quarts whole milk
⅔ cup fresh lemon juice
¼ cup chopped chives
Salt

Bring the milk to a boil in a large pot over high heat. Reduce the heat to medium and stir in the lemon juice. Reduce heat to low and stir constantly until curds begin to form. Remove from the heat.

Line a colander or sieve with cheesecloth. Spoon in the curdled milk and rinse under cool running water until the water runs clear. Place the colander over a bowl, cover with plastic wrap, and refrigerate for 8 hours to drain.

Discard the liquid, and stir the chives into the cheese. Season with salt to taste.

Store in an airtight container in the refrigerator for up to 1 week.

MAKES 1 CUP

PAPAYA KETCHUP

In Africa—where eating with your hands is an everyday experience—it's common to enrich the flavor of simple breads and grilled meats with a pungent dipping sauce. This one, which is laced with spicy serrano chilies, gets an exotic touch from the papaya. It makes a great accompaniment to grilled shrimp, chicken, and Roti, a puffy, deep-fried bread of Indian origin that is popular in East Africa (page 152).

2 teaspoons olive oil
1 garlic clove, minced
2 tomatoes, seeded and roughly chopped, or 1 cup chopped canned tomatoes
1 serrano chili, seeds and ribs removed, finely chopped
½ teaspoon sugar
1 tablespoon rice wine vinegar
1½ teaspoons soy sauce
½ teaspoon ground ginger
½ teaspoon Asian sesame oil
1 ripe papaya, peeled, seeded, and roughly chopped (about 1 cup)
Juice of 1 lime

Heat the olive oil in a large sauté pan over medium-high heat. Add the garlic and sauté for 2 to 3 minutes, until softened. Add the tomatoes, chili, sugar, and rice wine vinegar, reduce the heat to medium, and cook, stirring frequently, until the tomatoes are very soft, about 5 minutes. Remove from the heat and let cool slightly.

Transfer the tomato mixture to a blender. Add the soy sauce, ginger, sesame oil, papaya, and lime juice, and puree until smooth.

Store in a tightly covered container in the refrigerator for up to 5 days.

MAKES 2 CUPS

PICKLED GREEN AND YELLOW PAPAYAS

Before traveling to Africa I was familiar with sweet yellow papayas, which are commonly eaten for dessert. In Africa, as in Southeast Asian and Caribbean cuisines, green papayas are used just as often as the yellow. Unripe, they are almost like a vegetable, with a firm texture and an almost bitter taste. Here, green and yellow papayas are pickled together to create a relish that balances sweet and sour, and firm and soft.

½ cup sugar
2 shallots, sliced
1 Scotch bonnet chili, seeds and ribs removed, finely chopped
One 3-inch piece ginger, peeled and sliced
2 garlic cloves, minced
1 bay leaf
1 cup water
½ cup dry white wine
2 green papayas, peeled, seeded, and finely diced (about 2 cups)
1 ripe papaya, peeled, seeded, and finely diced (about 1 cup)
Juice of 1 lime

To make the pickling liquid, combine the sugar, shallots, chili, ginger, garlic, bay leaf, water, and wine in a medium saucepan and bring to a boil. Add the green papaya and simmer until tender, about 10 minutes. Remove from the heat and let cool.

Stir the yellow papaya into the green papaya mixture, then stir in the lime juice. Transfer the mixture to a container with a tight-fitting lid. Cover and refrigerate for at least 3 hours before serving.

Store in a tightly covered container in the refrigerator for up to 1 week.

MAKES 3 CUPS

PICKLED ONIONS

All around the world, onions are one of the most commonly pickled vegetables. These onions are made with chilies, giving them a spicy heat that you don't find in the commercially available, European-style onions at supermarkets.

2 tablespoons olive oil
1 large red onion, sliced ½ inch thick
2 Scotch bonnet chilies, seeds and ribs removed, chopped
2 small shallots, sliced
1 teaspoon mustard seeds
1 teaspoon nigella seeds (black onion seeds)
1 bay leaf
Grated zest and juice of 1 lime
2 tablespoons sugar
2 teaspoons salt
¾ cup white wine vinegar
2 cups water
2 garlic cloves, sliced
2 tarragon sprigs
3 scallions, cut into 4 pieces each

Heat the olive oil in a medium pot over high heat. Add the red onion and chilies and sauté for 2 minutes. Add the shallots, mustard seeds, nigella, bay leaf, lime zest, sugar, salt, vinegar, and the water and bring to a boil. Reduce the heat to low and simmer for 10 minutes.

Add the garlic and return to a boil. Stir in the lime juice, tarragon, and scallions and simmer for 5 minutes. Remove from heat and let cool.

Transfer to a container with a tight-fitting lid.

Store in a tightly covered container in the refrigerator for up to 1 month.

MAKES 2 CUPS

PIRI PIRI

Piri piri is the Swahili term for hot chili. It's also the name of the national dish of Mozambique, an extremely potent concoction used at tables around the country as a sauce for shellfish, fish, and chicken. Also known as pil pil and as pili pili, this fiery sauce is the first African food I ever had growing up in Sweden. In most cases, authentic piri piri is much too hot for American palates, so I've toned down the heat in this recipe. Because almost all of a chili pepper's heat is in the seeds and ribs, you can control the spiciness of the sauce by removing these hot spots or leaving them in, depending on your preference.

8 red bird's-eye chilies, seeds and ribs removed, chopped
½ cup fresh lemon juice
1 tablespoon chopped cilantro
1 tablespoon chopped parsley
2 garlic cloves
½ cup olive oil

Combine the chilies, lemon juice, cilantro, parsley, and garlic in a blender and puree until smooth. With the blender running, add the oil in a slow, steady stream and blend until well combined.

Store in an airtight container in the refrigerator for up to 2 weeks.

MAKES 1 CUP

PISTACHIO ROUILLE

s a chef, I love to blend my favorite elements from different cuisines. This rouille is a perfect example: to a classic French rouille made with potatoes and garlic, I add pistachios, one of the signature ingredients of North Africa. Use it to lend a creamy accent to lamb, pita bread, and dolmas.

2 tablespoons pistachios
1½ teaspoons Dijon mustard
2 cloves roasted garlic
½ cup mashed potatoes
Grated zest of 1 lemon
½ cup fresh lemon juice
1 tablespoon red wine vinegar
1 cup extra virgin olive oil
Salt and freshly ground black pepper

Heat a small sauté pan over medium heat. Add the pistachios and toast until fragrant and lightly browned, 30 to 60 seconds. Remove from the heat and let cool.

Transfer the pistachios to a blender. Add the mustard, garlic, potatoes, lemon zest, lemon juice, and vinegar and blend on low speed until smooth. With the blender running, add the olive oil in a slow, steady stream and blend until thickened. Season with salt and pepper.

Store in a tightly covered container in the refrigerator for up to 3 days.

MAKES 1¾ CUPS

PRESERVED CITRUS PEEL

Preserved lemons are an indispensable ingredient in Morocco, Algeria, and Tunisia, giving a fragrant, delicate citrus flavor to countless traditional dishes. This is a variation of the preserved lemons that are sold loose in souks (markets) throughout North Africa—the rinds of lemons, limes, oranges, and grapefruits are pickled in a sweet-salty solution for a mix of tart, sour, and sweet flavors. Don't skip any of the boiling and rinsing steps—the peel needs to be boiled in fresh water a total of three times to remove as much bitterness as possible.

2 lemons, scrubbed
2 limes, scrubbed
1 orange, scrubbed
1 grapefruit, scrubbed
1 cinnamon stick
1 tablespoon curry powder
1 red chili
1 teaspoon ground cardamom, preferably freshly ground
One 2-inch piece ginger, peeled and sliced
¼ cup salt
¼ cup honey

Using a sharp or serrated knife, cut away the colored peel from the lemons, limes, orange, and grapefruit, avoiding as much of the bitter white pith as possible. Reserve the fruit. Cut the peel into ½-inch-wide strips. Squeeze the juice from the fruit into a glass bowl; you should have about 2 cups of liquid. Set aside.

Place the peel and 2 cups water in a saucepan and bring to a boil; drain. Return the peel to the pan, add 2 cups of water, and bring to a boil; drain. Repeat once more, then drain.

Return the peel to the pan and add the reserved juice, the cinnamon stick, curry powder, chili, cardamom, ginger, salt, and honey. Bring to a boil, then reduce the heat and simmer for 5 to 6 minutes.

Remove from the heat and set aside to cool, then transfer to a quart jar or other container with a tight-fitting lid.

Store in a tightly sealed container in the refrigerator for up to 3 weeks.

MAKES 3 CUPS

RUM-PICKLED CHILIES

A few years ago I spent a week in Trinidad and Tobago, a Caribbean nation whose cuisine has been heavily influenced by the African diaspora, and was enchanted by the "bake 'n' shark" vendors selling grilled fish sandwiches up and down the beach. They all sell the same fish sandwich on a hollow pita-style bread, but what makes each vendor unique is the different pickled toppings the sandwiches are served with. The range of toppings I tried there inspired these Rum-Pickled Chilies, which make a great addition to any pantry.

1 tablespoon sugar
1 cup red wine vinegar
2 bay leaves
1 teaspoon coriander seeds
1 medium Spanish onion, sliced
2 garlic cloves, sliced
6 Scotch bonnet chilies, cut in half, seeds and ribs removed
2 jalapeño chilies, quartered, seeds and ribs removed
2 cups dark rum

Combine the sugar and vinegar in a small saucepan and bring to a boil. Add the bay leaves, coriander, onion, garlic, and chilies, bring to a simmer, and simmer for 4 minutes. Set aside to cool.

Stir in the rum to blend, then transfer to a quart jar or other container with a tight-fitting lid. Cover tightly and refrigerate for at least 24 hours before serving.

Store in the refrigerator in a tightly covered container for up to 3 weeks.

MAKES 4 CUPS

SAKAY

Over the past two thousand years, the island nation of Madagascar has been settled by a mix of African, Arab, Indonesian, and European peoples. All of them brought their own culinary influences and traditions, resulting in food that is full of flavor but simply prepared. Most recipes get a dose of heat from sakay, a fiery mash of dried red chilies, garlic, and ginger that is typically served on the side so diners can add as much or as little heat as they like.

¾ cup chili powder
1 tablespoon ground ginger
1½ teaspoons cayenne pepper
1 teaspoon ground cumin
4 garlic cloves, minced
2 teaspoons salt
1 cup peanut oil

Heat a medium sauté pan over medium heat. Add the chili powder, ginger, cayenne, cumin, and garlic and toast until fragrant, about 1 minute. Remove from the heat and let cool slightly.

Transfer the spice mixture to a blender, add the salt, and blend well on low speed. With the blender running, add the oil in a thin, steady stream and blend until a paste forms.

Store in the refrigerator in a tightly covered container for up to 2 weeks.

MAKES ABOUT 1⅓ CUPS

My memories of that day in Marrakech are very cinematic.

I VISITED MARRAKECH IN 1992, during what would be one of the most important years of my culinary education. I was working on a luxury cruise ship that traveled the world, stopping at different ports of call along the way to pick up ingredients for the next day's meal. I was twenty-two and fresh from Sweden.

Geographically, Morocco is very close to Europe, but the minute I set foot on the other side of the Mediterranean I knew I was in a completely different place. It had a mystique rooted in its culture that no European city has—I felt it in the ancient buildings, the elaborate, colorful mosaics that line the walls of mosques throughout the city, and the atmosphere that pervades the whole place. Marrakech is an old city, founded in the eleventh century, and donkeys and mules are still used to navigate streets too narrow for modern-day cars. The smells are distinctly earthy and evocative, and even the people look different—the men wear patterned baggy trousers and the women are swathed from head to toe in colorful fabrics and ornate jewelry.

But most memorable was the market in J'mal Fna, the city's old medina. It's a labyrinth lined with stalls that twists this way and that, and I lost my way a number of times as I wandered through the winding alleys. The streets were alive with shopkeepers and shoppers haggling over a jumble of leather goods, textiles, carpets, jewelry, food, clothing, and anything else you can imagine. On the sidelines, snake charmers, wildly whirling street dancers, fire eaters, and drummers competed for the attention of entranced tourists, while hurried locals plowed through this circuslike atmosphere in their rush to buy ingredients for that night's meal. There was a sense of urgency I'd never seen in a Western market, as if the people hurrying past wanted to say, "Get out of the way, things need to be sold, time is valuable."

I was an observer in this fascinating place, watching as an artisan in one corner of the market transferred brightly colored scarves and dresses from an enormous vat of dye set in the earth, while on the other side a shopkeeper weighed out salted lemons, spices, and olives. Around me, people bartered in a mishmash of languages, adding to the dreamlike sense of confusion. I felt like a foreigner and sensed that, in some way, I always would—that this was a culture I could never fully know or understand. It was both exhilarating and intimidating.

As for the food, it was a revelation. I'd read about ras al-hanout, the spice blend that Moroccan cuisine is built upon, but the exotic, intense hummus, breads, yogurt sauce, salted olives, and preserved lemons that we bought from vendors and ate in the street were as foreign to me as the veiled Muslim women who hurried through the market. This was my first taste of the beautifully balanced food of Morocco, with its delicate composition of couscous, rose water, pistachio, fragrant spices and dried fruits, and layers of seasonings reinforced in a beautiful composition of flavorful spreads, dips, and accompaniments.

My memories of that day in Marrakech are very cinematic, as if I had observed it all on a movie screen. It was a bewildering, kaleidoscopic swirl of colors, sounds, tastes, and smells that marked my entry to the alluring, mysterious Arab world.

THYME-ROASTED GARLIC

Roasting softens the harsh, assertive taste of raw garlic, giving it a delicate—almost sweet—taste that I like to use in sauces, dressings, dips and many other dishes. To make more, just multiply the recipe to whatever amount you need.

1 head garlic
3 thyme sprigs
2 tablespoons peanut oil

Preheat the oven to 300°F. Cut off the top ½ inch of the garlic head. Place the garlic and thyme on a square of foil and drizzle with the peanut oil. Wrap the foil around the garlic and place on a small baking sheet.

Roast the garlic for 40 minutes, or until the cloves are softened. Discard the thyme, and let cool.

To use, squeeze the pulp from the papery skin.

To store, wrap tightly in plastic wrap and refrigerate for up to 3 days.

MAKES 1½ TABLESPOONS

Citrus Cabbage Salad

Cucumber Salad

Grilled Seafood Salad with Yogurt Sauce

Herring-Potato Salad

Spiced Egg Salad

Dar Es Salaam, Tanzania

Warm Eggplant–Butternut Squash Salad

Warm Potato-Cod Salad

White Bean–Sardine Salad

Avocado Pap

Cassava-Avocado Mash

SALADS AND SIDES

Cauliflower Fritters

Corn Mashed Potatoes

Crispy Avocado

Mango Couscous

Pickled Cabbage

Pomegranate Rice

Red Rice

Red Penne

Shiro

Shiro-Stuffed Tomatoes

Yellow Rice

Spicy Plantain Chips

ridge also known as pap, by adding cornmeal to boiling water and cooking it until the water was absorbed. In Senegal, white rice or couscous made from cracked millet was served at every meal to accompany a variety of fish, meat, and vegetable stews. In other parts of West Africa, where fufu is the classic accompaniment to stews, I watched women patiently pounding boiled yams with a pestle or wooden spoon into a paste. Like ugali, that paste is then formed into small balls that are used as utensils to soak up sauce and scoop up pieces of meat, fish, or vegetables. While yams are the most common vegetable used for fufu, it is also made with cassava, plantains, green bananas, rice, beans, millet, sorghum, or cornmeal. In fact, fufu is so popular that I've even found boxes of fufu flour that make instant fufu at African markets here in the United States.

Like me, you may find that many of these staples are an acquired taste, but you can't help but appreciate that to millions of people around the continent these foods are a comforting source of nourishment that make an appearance at nearly every meal.

WARM EGGPLANT–BUTTERNUT SQUASH SALAD

My friend Hamid is originally from Morocco and has an encyclopedic knowledge of the foods of his homeland. He told me about one of his favorite meze, a warm salad made of eggplant and squash, known as zalouk. I've adapted his traditional recipe, adding the warm flavor of sumac and some zesty chilies to create a distinctive new meze that is an excellent appetizer when paired with pita, or a satisfying side to any roasted meat dish.

1½ tablespoons sumac (see page 5)
½ cup olive oil, divided
2 small butternut squash, peeled, seeded, and cut into 1-inch cubes (about 6 cups)
2 medium eggplants, peeled and cut into 2-inch cubes (about 6 cups)
One 3-inch piece ginger, peeled and sliced
Finely chopped zest of 1 lemon
6 garlic cloves, minced
2 red chilies, seeds and ribs removed, finely chopped
⅓ cup honey
½ cup water
1½ cups loosely packed baby spinach leaves
Juice of 2 limes
1 tablespoon chopped parsley
Salt

Preheat the oven to 350°F. Combine the sumac with 7 tablespoons of the olive oil in a small bowl. Toss the squash with half the oil, spread on a baking sheet in a single layer, and roast for about 40 minutes, until tender. After the squash has cooked for 15 minutes, toss the eggplant with the remaining oil and spread in a single layer on a second baking sheet. Place in the oven and roast until tender, about 25 minutes.

Meanwhile, heat the remaining 1 tablespoon olive oil in a large sauté pan over low heat. Add the ginger, lemon zest, garlic, and chilies and sauté until fragrant, about 5 minutes. Add the honey and water, stir to combine, and bring to a simmer. Simmer for 5 minutes. Remove from the heat and set aside.

Remove the vegetables from the oven and transfer to a large bowl. Add the spinach, the chili mixture, lime juice, and parsley and toss until the spinach wilts slightly. Season with salt.

4 TO 6 SERVINGS

WARM POTATO-COD SALAD

The Portuguese sailors who settled in Angola and Mozambique in the mid-sixteenth century introduced ingredients from both Europe and their New World colonies, blending them with the local cuisine and ingredients to create delicious new dishes. Baccalao, salted cod, is one Portuguese introduction that is now popular throughout the continent. Once a necessity for preserving the catch in pre-refrigeration days, salting is now used as a flavor enhancer. Here, it lends a briny taste to a warm potato salad that would make a great side dish at a barbecue.

8 ounces salt cod, cut into ½-inch slices
8 Yukon Gold potatoes (about 2½ pounds)
½ cup peanut oil, divided
1 red onion, thinly sliced
3 garlic cloves, chopped
2 red chilies, seeds and ribs removed, finely chopped
½ cup dry-roasted peanuts
2 teaspoons curry powder
1 tablespoon chopped parsley
½ head iceberg lettuce, shredded
Tamarind Vinaigrette (page 66)

Put the cod in a bowl, set in the sink, and rinse under cold running water for 30 minutes. Drain.

Meanwhile, preheat the oven to 350°F. Toss the potatoes with 2 tablespoons of the peanut oil. Place on a baking sheet and roast until tender, about 35 minutes. Let cool, then cut into ¼-inch slices.

Heat the remaining 6 tablespoons oil in a medium sauté pan over medium heat. Add the onion, garlic, chilies, and peanuts and cook, stirring, until the onion is softened and translucent, about 5 minutes. Add the cod and curry powder and cook, stirring constantly, until fragrant. Remove from the heat and set aside to cool.

Combine the potatoes and cod mixture in a large bowl. Add the parsley and lettuce, and toss with the vinaigrette.

6 SERVINGS

WHITE BEAN–SARDINE SALAD

An interesting salad has texture, flavor, and color. This salad has all the components I look for—the almonds and beans give it great texture, the sardines lend a nice, briny flavor, and the basil adds a splash of vibrant color. You can serve this as a side dish or even as a light meal on its own.

1 cup dried cannellini beans, soaked in cold water for 8 hours and drained
1 baking potato, peeled and cut into 2-inch chunks
1 medium yellow onion, cut into 2-inch chunks
½ cup olive oil
3 garlic cloves, sliced
1 tablespoon blanched whole almonds, roughly chopped
½ cup dry white wine
4 fresh sardine fillets
Juice of 1 lemon
2 teaspoons sumac (see page 5)
2 scallions, trimmed and chopped
2 tablespoons chopped basil

Place the beans in a large saucepan, cover with water, and bring to a boil. Reduce the heat to low and simmer for 30 minutes. Add the potato and onion, return to a simmer, and continue cooking until the potatoes and beans are tender, about another 25 minutes. Drain.

While the beans and potatoes are cooking, heat the olive oil in a large sauté pan over low heat. Add the garlic, almonds, and white wine and bring to a simmer. Reduce the heat to low and simmer for 5 minutes. Add the sardines, lemon juice, and sumac. Remove from the heat and let stand for 20 minutes.

Remove the sardines from the oil with a slotted spoon and set on paper towels to drain and cool; reserve the cooking oil. Cut the sardines into 1-inch slices.

Transfer half of the beans and potatoes to a food processor, add the reserved cooking oil, and process until smooth. Transfer to a bowl and fold in the remaining bean mixture, the scallions, and basil.

Mound the bean salad on a platter and top with the sardines.

4 SERVINGS

AVOCADO PAP

Mealie-pap, nshima, and ugali are different names for what is essentially the same food—a creamy cornmeal porridge similar to polenta—that is the basis of the diet of millions of people throughout East and Southern Africa. Because it can be rather bland and tasteless, I've dressed it up with chunks of corn, sweet tomatoes, and rich avocado, which transform it into a zippy side dish that maintains the taste and texture of the original.

1 cup very fine cornmeal (don't use stone-ground or coarse cornmeal)
4 cups water
1 teaspoon salt, or to taste
¼ teaspoon freshly ground black pepper
2 tablespoons olive oil
1 jalapeño chili, ribs and seeds removed, finely chopped
1 shallot, minced
1 cup corn kernels
1 ripe tomato, chopped
1 avocado, pitted, peeled, and cut into ½-inch dice
2 scallions, trimmed and chopped

Combine the cornmeal with the water in a large saucepan, stir well, and bring to a boil over medium heat, stirring constantly. Add the salt and pepper, reduce the heat, and simmer for 20 to 25 minutes, stirring constantly to break up any lumps and prevent burning, until thickened. Remove from the heat and set aside.

Heat the olive oil in a large sauté pan over medium-high heat. Add the jalapeño, shallot, corn, and tomatoes and sauté for 2 minutes. Stir in the avocado and scallions and remove from the heat.

Fold the tomato-avocado mixture into the cornmeal, adjust the salt if necessary, and serve.

4 SERVINGS

MTN
MTN

MANGO COUSCOUS

Muna, an acquaintance from Libya, tells of visiting her aunt back home and sitting outside with her and the neighborhood women as they made couscous. She described the hypnotic process of the women rolling semolina dough in their hands, crumbling it into smaller chunks with their fingers, then rubbing the crumbs into smaller pieces until they were the right size. They made huge batches at a time, laying the grains in the sun to dry, then steaming them and drying them again. Fortunately, commercially made couscous is easy to find in stores and of very high quality, so you can enjoy this lovely dish without spending days preparing the grains.

1 cup couscous
2 tablespoons olive oil, divided
1 garlic clove, minced
1 mango, peeled, pitted, and cut into 1-inch cubes (about 1 cup)
1 jalapeño chili, seeds and ribs removed, finely chopped
½ cup raisins
1 ripe tomato, chopped
Juice of 1 lime
¼ cup loosely packed small cilantro sprigs, chopped
¼ cup loosely packed small parsley sprigs, chopped
Salt

Prepare the couscous according to the package directions. Set aside.

Heat 1 tablespoon of the olive oil in a large sauté pan over high heat. Add the garlic, mango, and jalapeño and sauté until the mango begins to color lightly. Stir in the remaining tablespoon of olive oil, the couscous, raisins, tomato, lime juice, cilantro, and parsley and toss to heat through. Season with salt.

Serve hot or at room temperature.

4 SERVINGS

RED RICE

In Dakar I was served a rice dish that had a startlingly vivid red hue and a pleasingly intense flavor. The color and taste came from shrimp powder, made from dried shrimp pounded by hand to a fine, dusty powder, then sifted to remove any shells. Shrimp powder has limited availability in the United States, but it's worth seeking out at African or Asian markets. If you can't find it, you can get a similar color by adding a tablespoon of tomato paste along with the tomato juice.

¼ cup peanut oil
1 small red onion, sliced
1 jalapeño chili, seeds and ribs removed, finely chopped
2 teaspoons shrimp powder (optional)
3 garlic cloves, minced
2 tomatoes, chopped, or 1 cup chopped canned tomatoes
1 teaspoon chili powder
1 cup short-grain white rice
1½ teaspoons salt
2 thyme sprigs
1 cup tomato juice
2 cups water
¼ cup loosely packed cilantro sprigs, chopped

Heat the peanut oil in a large saucepan over high heat. When the oil shimmers, add the onion and cook until translucent, 5 to 7 minutes. Add the jalapeño, shrimp powder, if using, and garlic and sauté for 1 minute. Reduce the heat to low, stir in the tomatoes and chili powder, and cook for 10 minutes, or until the oil separates from the tomatoes.

Add the rice and stir to coat. Stir in the salt, thyme, tomato juice, and water and bring to a boil. Reduce the heat to low, cover, and simmer for 15 minutes.

Remove the pan from the heat and stir in the cilantro. Replace the cover and let sit for 10 minutes, until all the liquid is absorbed.

4 TO 6 SERVINGS

SPICY PLANTAIN CHIPS

Plantains, the large, starchy cousin of the banana, are a staple throughout Africa and used in much the same way as potatoes are here. These chips make an excellent snack before a meal. Deep-fried plantains can often be a little dull and starchy, but by frying them in spiced butter and oil, and dusting them with a spicy curry powder, they get a lively, complex flavor. Green, unripe plantains make the best chips because they are firmer and hold up better during cooking.

2 green plantains
1 tablespoon curry powder
1 teaspoon confectioners' sugar
1 teaspoon salt
1 cup Spiced Butter (page 34) **or ½ pound (2 sticks) unsalted butter**
About 2 cups canola oil

Peel the plantains (see page 5) and slice as thin as possible with a mandoline, peeler, or sharp knife. Place in a bowl, cover with cold water, and let soak for 10 minutes to wash away excess starch. (The starch can cause the slices to stick together during frying.) Drain, rinse, and blot thoroughly dry with paper towels.

Meanwhile, combine the curry powder, sugar, and salt in a small bowl.

Melt the spiced butter in a large deep pot over medium heat, then add enough oil to come to a depth of 1½ inches. Increase the heat to medium-high and heat to the oil 350°F. Working in batches, carefully lower the plantains into the oil with a slotted spoon and fry, stirring occasionally to prevent the slices from sticking together, until evenly browned, about 4 minutes. Remove from the oil and drain on paper towels. Dust with the curry and sugar mixture and serve immediately.

MAKES ABOUT 2½ CUPS

MTN
MORE

Callaloo

Chicken and Shrimp Soup

Chicken-Peanut Stew

Crab Soup

Wandie's Place, Johannesburg, South Africa

Cod Stew with Sesame Seeds

Grilled Tilapia–Avocado Soup

SOUPS AND STEWS

Lentil Stew

Plantain-Coconut Stew

Quail–Foie Gras Soup

Spicy Crayfish Boil

Spicy Tilapia Stew

Squid with Corn-Tomato Soup

Stir-Fried Beef Stew

Trout with Spinach Sauce

IN MOST OF AFRICA, THE FINER CUTS OF MEATS, POULTRY, AND FISH ARE RESERVED for special occasions and celebrations. When it comes to day-to-day meals, small amounts of inexpensive meats or other protein are stretched with vegetables and liquid to create a mind-bogglingly diverse range of soups and stews that are dished up with filling starchy sides.

All cultures have their own version of so-called peasant food, which uses cheap and available ingredients to make the more expensive ones go further. In many ways, I think African cooking is poor man's cooking at its finest. Home cooks have learned to use common, inexpensive ingredients—peanuts, chilies, beans, tomatoes, onions, okra, and greens—to transform scraps of meat, fish, or chicken into mouthwatering stews like chep-bu-jen, sukuma wiki, or callaloo. Stews are just as important from a sociological point of view. Family ties have remained strong in African life, with generations often living under the same roof in many homes. Because people tend to live together in large groups, the communal nature of stews is appealing for women who have to cook in bulk for their families, helping to preserve age-old traditions and ways of life. In fact, in rural areas you often still see women preparing stews outdoors, as they have done for centuries: in a pot perched on a three-rock stove.

Although you find stews throughout the continent, regional variations are striking and give insight into each area's history and culinary style. In the Maghreb, tagines are accented with the sweetness of dried dates and apricots in the style of the Arabs who settled the region, while in the southern parts of West Africa, stews are finished with red palm oil and seasoned with chilies. Ethiopia's many stews are laced with fiery berbere, while more delicate Indian and Asian spices flavor the stews of East Africa and South Africa's Malay cooking. Many of these stews are so well loved they are considered the national dishes.

This chapter features both traditional soups and stews and my own variations; I use African ingredients and flavors to develop elegant new dishes like Chicken and Shrimp Soup or Spicy Crayfish Boil. Use them to create an authentic African experience in your home: turn on some Senegalese music, set out a communal serving bowl of stew and a platter of fufu or ugali or pita, and take a little trip to Africa without ever leaving your house.

Wandie's Place is the place to be.

IN CASABLANCA, EVERYBODY WENT TO RICK'S, but when you are in Soweto—the sister city of Johannesburg—Wandie's Place is the place to be. Wandie's is one of the most famous restaurants in Africa, attracting foreign politicians, visiting celebrities, and busloads of tourists who come for the delicious black South African fare and the charming company of owner Wandie Ndaba. But it wasn't always this way. Today Wandie's may be the local hot spot, but like everything I saw in Soweto, the restaurant has evolved over the years to fit into the ever-changing neighborhood that surrounds it.

Wandie's began in 1981 as an illegal local shebeen (saloon) run out of Wandie's house. At the time, Soweto, which is short for "South Western Townships," was a hotbed of anti-apartheid activities—it's the only place in the world with one street where two Nobel peace prize winners, Desmond Tutu and Nelson Mandela, once lived—and Wandie's was in constant danger of being shut down by a police raid. By 1991, as apartheid was coming to its inevitable end, Wandie received a license for his joint and began serving food, carving out a niche for himself in the new up-and-coming neighborhood. As his restaurant gained popularity, Wandie added an extension to his house to accommodate the hundreds of locals and tourists who come to eat every day. Today, Wandie is one of

COD STEW WITH SESAME SEEDS

I met Muna—a woman who was born in Libya, raised in France, and now lives in New York—at an art opening, and she generously shared with me her memories of Libyan food. As Libya is one of the few African countries colonized by Italy, its food is a lot more Italian-influenced than in Morocco and Tunisia, where stews and savory dishes tend to be sweeter. This fish stew takes its flavor reference points from the Italian-based traditions of Libyan cooking, featuring tomatoes, garlic, and za'atar.

1 cup blanched whole almonds
4 garlic cloves, cut in half
1 teaspoon grated ginger
6 tomatoes, roughly chopped, or 3 cups roughly chopped canned tomatoes
2 jalapeño chilies, finely chopped, seeds and ribs removed
2 teaspoons Za'atar (page 37)
4 cups chicken stock
Salt
2 green plantains, peeled (see page 5) and diced
1 cup cooked black beans, rinsed if canned
10 ounces morning glory (see page 4) or spinach
2 pounds cod fillet, cut into 1-inch pieces
2 tablespoons olive oil
1 teaspoon sesame oil (not toasted)
2 tablespoons sesame seeds
Juice of 2 limes, or to taste

Toast the almonds in a large pot over low heat until golden brown and fragrant, about 5 minutes. Add the garlic and ginger and cook, stirring constantly, until aromatic, about 1 minute. Add the tomatoes, jalapeños, za'atar, chicken stock, and 1 teaspoon salt and bring to a simmer over medium-high heat. Reduce the heat and simmer gently for 25 minutes.

Stir in the plantains and simmer for 10 minutes. Stir in the beans, then add the morning glory and cod, and simmer for 5 minutes. Remove from the heat, cover, and let sit until the stew begins to thicken, about 15 minutes.

Meanwhile, heat the olive oil and sesame oil in a small sauté pan over low heat. Add the sesame seeds and sauté, swirling the seeds in the pan, until golden and fragrant, 5 to 7 minutes. Remove from the heat.

Just before serving, gently fold the sesame seeds into the stew, then season with the lime juice and salt to taste.

6 SERVINGS

WALE -ST
WAAL STR
WALE ST

Corn Bread

Cumin Braai Bread

Curry Chapatis

Dried Fruit Bread

Injera

Addis Ababa, Ethiopia

Honey Bread

Pita Bread

Roti

Toasted Peanut Bread

BREADS, DUMPLINGS, AND SANDWICHES

Crab Burgers

Chili-Spiced Lamb Sandwiches

Egg Sandwiches

Lamb and Veal Kefta with Tomato-Cucumber Salad

Potato-Lentil Dumplings

Fried Fish Baguette

Vegetable Samosas

Zanzibari "Pizzas"

Spicy Tuna on Chapatis

TRAVELING THROUGH AFRICA IS A BIT LIKE TAKING a greatest-bread-hits-of-the-world tour: in Morocco I tore into Middle Eastern–style pitas and flatbreads, in Tanzania I dipped Indian chapatis into stews and sauces, in Ethiopia I tasted authentic injera for the first time, in South Africa I tasted traditional Zulu steamed bread, and in Senegal I met up with two familiar favorites, the French baguette and croissant.

Breads play an important role in African cooking, where they are just as valued for their taste as they are for their belly-filling capabilities. Breads are cheap and flavorful, making them an important part of the daily meal in places where finding economical solutions is a necessity. In some places, breads like chapatis, pitas, and injera even take the place of utensils, used to scoop up stews and dips and sauces while adding bulk to every meal.

In many places, I saw dough stuffed with meats or vegetables to make cheap and easy snacks, like the samosas I had in Cape Town's Muslim Bo-Kaap district. Perhaps the most unusual variation on this theme, though, was the "Zanzibari Pizza" I bought from a street vendor in Stone Town: a chapati stuffed with eggs and quickly fried on an outdoor grill.

Sandwiches, too, are everywhere as convenient grab-it-and-go meals. One memory from my visit to Ethiopia is of breakfast at Café Parisian in Addis Ababa. I stood in line to get an omelet sandwich made of eggs, milk, jalapeño, and berbere on honey bread that was so heavy and filling I was set until way after lunchtime.

The global flavors of African breads and sandwiches inspired the recipes in this chapter. Try a Crab Burger or the Potato-Lentil Dumplings when you want a break from a run-of-the-mill ham and cheese sandwich. As for the breads, add a touch of the continent to your next dinner party by dispensing with utensils and letting your guests dip injera, pita, or roti to scoop up delicious tidbits, bringing the laid-back and relaxed atmosphere of Africa into your dining room.

Making injera is truly an art.

AS WE TRAVELED THROUGH AFRICA, my companions and I ate well at every stop along the way. But by the time we got to our last stop, Tanzania, all my photographer and friend Gediyon wanted was injera.

Gediyon was born and raised in Ethiopia, where injera is such an important food that "Have you eaten injera today?" is a common greeting among Ethiopians. As I've mentioned earlier, this sour, spongy bread is made from teff, a tiny, nutrient-dense grain native to Ethiopia that is just becoming available in the United States. Our quest for injera in Dar es Salaam brought us to Addis in Dar, the only Ethiopian restaurant in the city, and while the meal helped to appease Gediyon's longing, he still hungered for what he calls the "real thing." Ethiopian expatriates can argue for days about the superiority of injera in their homeland. Just as California wines are better in Napa Valley and pasta is better in Italy, the combination of the people, the smells, the surroundings, and the taste makes injera better in Ethiopia.

Making injera is truly an art, and a time-consuming one at that, as I learned on my first trip to Ethiopia. While some families do still make their own injera, most buy it from tef terras—small huts that specialize in making injera. I visited one of these injera houses for my lesson. The small, single-roomed hut was run as a sort of co-op by five Ethiopian women who were true artisans in their craft. I watched as they stood under the hot sun pounding the teff grains with a stone into a nice, fine powder and then sifted the flour to remove any impurities. The flour was then made into a dough and set aside for three days to ferment—this step gives injera its distinctive sour taste—before being cooked in an enormous skillet over a wood fire.

One of the women offered to let me try my hand at making injera. Standing behind a large round pan set atop a clay oven, she worked quickly, pouring the fermented dough from a dented old tomato can in a spiral onto the hot pan, then covering the griddle with a lid and sealing the edges with a damp rag. After a few minutes, she lifted the lid and removed the injera from the pan, adding it to the growing stack of injera at her side. When I finally took my turn, I couldn't keep up with her rhythm and technique. I wasn't able to master the spiral in one swift motion, and the first dozen or so pieces I made were thick and misshapen. She'd been making injera her whole life and cheerfully told me it would take some time for me to get it right.

Before the injera is sold, each piece is folded into neat, compact quarters for serving. Ethiopians still laugh over the story of a nineteenth-century European visitor who mistakenly took a folded piece of injera for a napkin and set it on his lap, but those unfamiliar with the traditional Ethiopian place setting could easily understand his mistake. At the Ethiopian table, a piece of injera is unfolded and draped over the table, like a tablecloth, and a variety of stews are ladled over the top. Diners tear off pieces of injera from a pile of folded injeras to scoop up the stews, eventually eating the actual "tablecloth" that has soaked up all the sauce.

I'd eaten and enjoyed injera many times before this hot summer day, but my lesson gave me a new respect for the tradition and hard work that goes into making Ethiopia's signature bread. I'm reminded of it every time I use injera to scoop up a mouthful of doro wett, tibs wett, or ayib.

CHILI-SPICED LAMB SANDWICHES

When I was growing up in Sweden, my parents very rarely let my sisters and me eat at fast food restaurants. But they had no issue with our eating the takeout sandwiches sold by recent immigrants from the Middle East and eastern Africa. This lamb sandwich, served with a sauce deliciously tart with lemon and tangy with olives and mint, is typical of those I ate as a boy and later saw on my travels through North Africa, where lamb is the most common meat.

2 tablespoons Harissa (page 30)
½ cup olive oil
1½ pounds boneless lamb loin, cut into 1-inch cubes
1 medium red onion, sliced
1½ cup chicken stock or water
2 lemons, cut into quarters
1 cup chickpeas, soaked in cold water for 24 hours and drained
4 tomatoes, diced, or 2 cups chopped canned tomatoes
2 cinnamon sticks
4 garlic cloves, cut into thirds
½ cup fresh lemon juice
½ cup black olives, pitted and cut in half
4 mint sprigs, leaves only, minced
Salt and freshly ground black pepper
2 pita breads, warmed
Chickpea-Eggplant Dip (page 42)

Mix the harissa and olive oil in a large bowl. Add the lamb cubes and toss to coat.

Heat a large sauté pan over high heat. Add the lamb and onion and sear on all sides, about 3 minutes per side. Remove the lamb from the pan with a slotted spoon.

Add the chicken stock, lemons, chickpeas, tomatoes, cinnamon, and garlic to the same pan and stir well. Bring to a simmer, stirring with a wooden spoon to scrape up any browned bits on the bottom of the pan. Reduce the heat and simmer, uncovered, for 25 minutes.

Return the lamb to the pan, add the lemon juice and olives, and simmer for 5 minutes. Stir in the mint and cook for 2 more minutes. Remove the cinnamon sticks, and season with salt and pepper. Remove from the heat.

Slice the pita breads in half. Spread the dip inside each pocket, and, using a slotted spoon, stuff the pockets with the lamb and vegetables.

4 SERVINGS

EGG SANDWICHES

Many people stay away from street food when they are traveling. Not me. I love experiencing a culture through its street food, because it gives me insight that I'd never find at fancier, tourist-oriented restaurants. One morning after an early jog on the beach in Dakar, I stopped at one of the local food stands for breakfast. The owner served just one thing—an egg sandwich—from his stand, which consisted of a table with a gas-fired burner, a coffee kettle, and a few chairs. Men stood in line for their coffee and sandwiches, then sat down at a little table nearby to eat and converse before going to work. I thought it was a perfectly delicious way to start the day.

2 tomatoes, thinly sliced
¼ head iceberg lettuce, shredded
2 small red onions, 1 sliced, 1 cut into ¼-inch dice
6 large eggs
¾ cup milk
½ teaspoon chili powder
½ teaspoon salt
2 tablespoons canola oil
2 tablespoons Chili Mayonnaise (page 45)
1 baguette, split lengthwise and cut into quarters

Combine the tomatoes, lettuce, and sliced onion in a bowl. Set aside.

Whisk the eggs, diced onion, milk, chili powder, and salt together in a separate bowl. Heat 1 tablespoon of the oil in a large sauté pan over high heat. Add half the egg mixture and stir until the eggs are set, then flip and cook on the other side until golden brown. Transfer to a warmed plate and repeat with the remaining eggs.

Spread a thin layer of mayonnaise on the cut sides of the baguette. Divide the eggs in half, and put on the bottom halves of the bread. Top with the tomato, lettuce, and onion and serve.

4 SERVINGS

LAMB AND VEAL KEFTA WITH TOMATO-CUCUMBER SALAD

Morocco is a friendly, frenzied, energizing place—open-air bazaars are everywhere, crowded with stalls selling stunning rugs, woodwork, and jewelry, and food vendors hawking a range of traditional Moroccan foods line the streets to cater to the throngs of people shopping at the markets. One of my favorite street foods was kefta—spiced, cigar-shaped meat patties. Here, I use ground lamb and veal and shape them into patties to serve in pita bread with a spicy tomato-cucumber salad.

3 tablespoons olive oil
2 medium Spanish onions, minced
3 garlic cloves, minced
3 serrano chilies, seeds and ribs removed, finely chopped
1 teaspoon ground coriander
1 teaspoon ground cumin
12 ounces ground lamb
12 ounces ground veal
1½ teaspoons garam masala
1 teaspoon dried oregano
1 teaspoon salt
8 pita breads
Tomato-Cucumber Salad (recipe follows)

Heat the olive oil in a large sauté pan over medium-high heat. When the oil begins to shimmer, add the onions, garlic, and chilies and sauté until the onions are softened, about 7 minutes. Stir in the coriander and cumin, and remove from the heat. Let cool.

Combine the lamb, veal, chili-onion mixture, garam masala, oregano, and salt in a large bowl and mix with your hands. Shape the meat into 8 patties, 3 inches in diameter and 1 inch thick.

Heat a large skillet over medium-high heat. Add the patties, in batches if necessary, and sauté for 5 minutes on each side, until deeply browned and cooked through.

To serve, slice the pita breads open halfway. Put 1 tablespoon of the salad in each bread, add a patty, and top with an additional 2 tablespoons salad.

8 SERVINGS

TOMATO-CUCUMBER SALAD

1 large ripe beefsteak tomato, peeled, seeded, and cut into ¼-inch dice
½ cucumber, peeled, seeded, and cut into ¼-inch dice
2 garlic cloves, minced
2 to 3 pickled jalapeño chilies, finely chopped
1½ tablespoons plain yogurt
Juice of 1 lemon
Salt and freshly ground black pepper

Combine the tomatoes, cucumber, garlic, and chilies in a bowl. Gently fold in the yogurt and lemon juice. Just before serving, season with salt and pepper.

VEGETABLE SAMOSAS

The steep, narrow, cobbled streets of the Bo-Kaap, Cape Town's Muslim district, are a picturesque jumble of brightly colored nineteenth-century homes, shops, mosques, and shrines perched on the slopes of Signal Hill overlooking Table Bay. After exploring a neighborhood spice shop with a mind-boggling assortment of bulk spices, we stopped for dinner at Biesmiellah. One of the neighborhood's oldest and best-known restaurants, they served the flakiest, most delicious samosas I've ever tasted, which inspired this recipe.

4 teaspoons ground turmeric
1 teaspoon ground ginger
1 teaspoon ground cinnamon
1½ cups all-purpose flour
2 teaspoons salt
2 tablespoons peanut oil
1 cup water
Juice of 2 lemons
Vegetable Filling (recipe follows)
About 4 cups peanut oil for deep-frying

Toast the turmeric, ginger, and cinnamon in a small sauté pan over high heat until fragrant, 30 to 60 seconds. Remove from the heat and let cool.

Sift together the flour, toasted spices, and salt into a large bowl, and make a well in the center. Pour the oil, water, and lemon juice into the well. Slowly stir the flour into the liquids until all the liquid has been absorbed.

Turn the dough out onto a floured work surface and knead until it is smooth and elastic and begins to form into a ball, about 10 minutes. Transfer to a bowl, cover with a damp cloth or oiled plastic wrap, and let rest in a warm, draft-free place for 20 minutes.

Divide the dough into 12 equal pieces. One at a time, roll out each piece on a floured work surface to a 6-inch circle. Place a generous tablespoon of the filling in the center of each circle of dough. Brush the edges with a little water, and fold the dough over the filling to make a half-moon. Crimp the edges with a fork to seal. Let rest for 30 minutes.

Heat 3 inches of peanut oil in a deep pot to 350°F. Working in batches, carefully add the samosas and fry, stirring occasionally, until golden, about 10 minutes. Remove from the oil with a slotted spoon and drain on paper towels.

Serve with Yogurt Dip (page 73) and Mango Sambal (page 64).

MAKES 12 PASTRIES

VEGETABLE FILLING

2 tablespoons olive oil
1 small yellow onion, sliced
2 small Yukon Gold potatoes (about 8 ounces total), peeled and cut into 2-inch cubes
1 tablespoon Green Curry Paste (page 26)
1 carrot, peeled and cut into 2-inch pieces
2 garlic cloves, minced
½ head cauliflower, cut into florets
½ cup coconut milk
½ cup water
Juice of 1 lime

Heat the oil in a large sauté pan, preferably nonstick, over medium heat. Add the onion and potatoes and sauté until the onion is translucent, about 5 minutes. Reduce the heat to low, add the curry paste, carrot, and garlic, and cook, stirring occasionally, for 10 minutes. Add the cauliflower, coconut milk, and water, bring to a simmer, and simmer for 15 minutes. Stir in the lime juice, then transfer to a bowl and set aside to cool.

Mash the filling to a chunky puree with a fork.

Apple-Squash Fritters

Black-Eyed Peas

Candied Yams and Plantains

Chunky Mashed Vegetables

Creamed Swiss Chard

Merkato, Addis Ababa, Ethiopia

Crispy Vegetables

Mustard Greens and Corn

Falafel with Quick Tomato Sauce

VEGETABLES

Pumpkin Mash

Palaver Sauce

Roasted Eggplant and Plantains

Sautéed Morning Glory

Sautéed Vegetables

Spicy Okra

Vegetable Tagine

Warm Cabbage

IF I HAD TO NAME ONE FOOD SERVED IN EVERY COUNTRY THROUGHOUT AFRICA, it would have to be greens. Collard greens, spinach, pumpkin leaves, cassava leaves . . . no matter where I went, greens had a place of prominence on the table.

Vegetables are used to add flavor to a meal, lend it texture, or sometimes even take the place of meat. In a society where meat is an expensive luxury and religious beliefs call for numerous fasting days, they provide an inexpensive way to add flair and variety. The breadth is astonishing, including those I use daily—eggplants, corn, tomatoes, peas, pumpkin, beans, okra, onions, garlic, cabbage, carrots, yams, and potatoes—and the not-so-well-known, like cassava, cocoyams, and bush greens. Whenever possible, practical cooks find a way to use every part of the plant, serving up the leaves of pumpkin and cassava plants in rich and filling stews and soups. Fruit, both wild and cultivated, is abundant in the warm tropical climate of sub-Saharan Africa, so they are put to use as well: I saw avocados, plantains, tomatoes, mangoes, baobabs, and papayas used in everything from soups, stews, and sauces to salads and sides.

Just as striking as the variety was the freshness of the fruits and vegetables I had there. Food that's been flown in from another hemisphere is rare; much of the population is still rural, scraping out a living by growing crops and selling them daily at the nearby market, so many of the vegetables I feasted on had been plucked just a day or two before. They're also grown organically, so they don't necessarily look as pretty, but they taste better.

African food has spread all over the world, a fact particularly obvious with vegetables. Just as I noticed a clear musical pattern between West Africa and the Caribbean, I also discerned similarities between the vegetables: for example, callaloo, the national dish of Trinidad and Tobago, clearly derives from West African cooking traditions. The same is true of such soul food classics as Hoppin' John and gumbo, which were created by slaves brought to the American South from West Africa.

The recipes in this chapter stem from very traditional recipes based on what I ate, saw, and heard as I traveled, such as Spicy Okra, Pumpkin Mash, and Palaver Sauce, to new creations using African food as a starting point, like Creamed Swiss Chard and Apple-Squash Fritters. For the best-tasting results, shop like an African: whenever possible, go to your local farmers' market and buy organic ingredients fresh from the earth.

APPLE-SQUASH FRITTERS

South Africa's Cape Malay cuisine always features something sweet. These crispy fritters highlight hearty, autumnal flavors that make an excellent accompaniment to game or chicken dishes. If you want some extra sweetness, dust them with a light coating of confectioners' sugar.

2 apples, peeled, cored, and cut into 2-inch cubes
2 pounds butternut squash, peeled, seeded, and cut into 1-inch cubes
4 garlic cloves, peeled
3 tablespoons olive oil
2 tablespoons sugar
1 teaspoon ground cinnamon
2 teaspoons garam masala
1 teaspoon salt
1 tablespoon cornstarch
⅓ cup plus 2 tablespoons all-purpose flour
2 cups peanut oil

Preheat the oven to 350°F. Arrange the apples, squash, and garlic on a baking sheet and brush with the olive oil. Roast for 15 minutes, until the garlic is tender, then remove and reserve the garlic cloves. Return the baking sheet to the oven and roast the apples and squash for 20 minutes, or until soft.

Mix together the sugar and cinnamon in a small bowl. Set aside.

Transfer the roasted apples and squash to a bowl, add the garlic, and mash with a fork. Stir in the garam masala, salt, cornstarch, and ⅓ cup of the flour; the dough will be very soft. With wet hands, shape the dough into 2-inch balls. Roll the balls in the remaining 2 tablespoons flour.

Heat the peanut oil in a deep pot to 350°F. Working in batches, carefully add the fritters and fry, turning occasionally, until golden brown, about 4 minutes. Remove the fritters with a slotted spoon and drain on paper towels. Sprinkle with the cinnamon sugar and serve immediately.

4 TO 6 SERVINGS

BLACK-EYED PEAS

Here in the United States, black-eyed peas are best known as the basis for the Southern rice-and-beans dish Hoppin' John, which is thought to bring luck and prosperity when eaten on New Year's Day. But in fact this bean originated in West Africa, where it is a popular ingredient in any number of dishes. My friend Keke is from Ghana, and his mother told me about one of her favorite dishes, red-red, a stew of fried plantains and boiled black-eyed peas that is common at Ghanian tables. This version of black-eyed peas is made distinctive with coconut milk, ginger, and berbere. It's a great accompaniment to grilled meat or fish.

1 cup black-eyed peas, soaked in cold water for 8 hours and drained

¼ cup Spiced Butter (page 34) **or 4 tablespoons (½ stick) unsalted butter**

1 medium red onion, sliced

2 tomatoes, chopped

1 Scotch bonnet chili, seeds and ribs removed, finely chopped

2 garlic cloves, chopped

One 1-inch piece ginger, peeled and chopped

2 teaspoons Berbere (page 12) **or chili powder**

1 cup coconut milk

1 teaspoon ground turmeric

1 cup chicken stock

1 teaspoon salt

2 cilantro sprigs, chopped

1 scallion, trimmed and sliced

Combine the peas with 4 cups water in a large saucepan and simmer, uncovered, for 45 minutes, or until tender. Drain and set aside.

Melt the butter in a deep pot over medium heat. Add the onion, tomatoes, and chili and sauté until the onion is translucent, about 10 minutes. Add the garlic, ginger, berbere, and coconut milk and bring to a simmer. Stir in the turmeric and chicken stock and bring to a simmer, then reduce the heat to low and simmer, uncovered, until the sauce thickens, about 20 minutes.

Add the peas and salt and simmer until most of the liquid is absorbed, about 20 minutes.

Stir in the cilantro and scallion, and serve.

4 TO 6 SERVINGS

CANDIED YAMS AND PLANTAINS

Legend has it that the word "yam" comes from a misunderstanding between Portuguese slave traders and a group of workers who were digging up the tubers in the area that today is Guinea. When asked what the tubers were called, the Africans answered, "Nyami"—"something to eat" in their language—and the name stuck.

Yams and plantains are two of the staples of West African cooking. In this recipe, I play off the natural sweetness of both for a hearty, filling side dish that's a great complement to slow-cooked meats and game.

2 medium yams (about 2 pounds total), peeled and cut into 6 pieces each

3 tablespoons Spiced Butter (page 34) **or unsalted butter, melted**

¼ cup soy sauce

1 cup orange juice

¼ cup honey

½ teaspoon ground cumin

½ teaspoon ground ginger

2 medium green plantains, peeled (see page 5) **and cut into 3-inch pieces**

Preheat the oven to 350°F. Arrange the yams in a baking dish and brush with the butter. Roast for 20 minutes.

While the yams are roasting, combine the soy sauce, orange juice, honey, cumin, and ginger in a small bowl and whisk until well blended.

Add the plantains to the yams and pour ½ cup of the orange juice glaze over the plantains and yams. Return to the oven and roast for another 20 minutes, or until tender, brushing every 5 to 10 minutes with the remaining glaze.

8 SERVINGS

Merkato is the produce market, where local farmers bring their fruits and vegetables to sell at one of the thousands of busy stalls.

My first impression was one of utter chaos. People darted everywhere to buy and sell, and there was zero tolerance for onlookers. Work begins before 4:30 A.M., when that day's produce is unloaded and sold to the guys who run the stalls. Once that trading is finished, customers start flocking to the market to buy food for their families, streaming in until late afternoon.

The Merkato is amazing, but it's by no means uncommon. Even the smallest African villages have a tiny vegetable market where local farmers sell their harvest and the locals gather to shop, do business, or just visit. And the markets in many of the larger cities are legendary. Since the end of the fourteenth century, Cairo's Khan al Khalili market has been the city's center of commerce. Today, it's an enticing array of one-stop shopping for everything you need, from household goods and tea to melons, gold and silver jewelry,

and bootleg technology. To the west, residents of Marrakech buy vegetables, rugs, shoes, and anything else they could possibly need at colorful souks that made me feel like I'd stepped into another century. Each market I visited throughout the continent was different, but one thing always held true: bargaining was part of the process of shopping, and no shop or stall owner expected to be paid the amount they first gave you. I quickly got into the act and had as much fun bargaining as I did shopping.

Here in the United States, I often hear people say that San Francisco has the best food markets—beautiful, locally grown fruits and vegetables, neatly organized and arranged in spotless markets. But as I look back on the loud, vibrant, spectacular markets I saw in each of the places I visited, my vote goes for the bustling, busy, enchanting markets of Africa.

FALAFEL WITH QUICK TOMATO SAUCE

Falafel is said to have originated in Egypt, where it is now one of the national dishes. In Egypt it is typically made with dried broad beans but I prefer the nutty taste you get from chickpeas. Because falafel tends to be dry, I like to serve it with a dipping sauce. The flavor-rich tomato sauce that is drizzled over these falafel is a nice change of pace from the tahini sauce that traditionally accompanies it.

1 cup dried chickpeas, soaked in cold water for 24 hours and drained
1 small Spanish onion, quartered
3 garlic cloves, lightly crushed and peeled
1 teaspoon ground coriander
1 tablespoon ground cumin
1 teaspoon chili powder
½ cup chopped parsley
2½ teaspoons salt
½ teaspoon freshly ground black pepper, or to taste
½ teaspoon baking soda
1 tablespoon fresh lemon juice
About 4 cups peanut oil for deep-frying
1 egg , if needed

Combine the chickpeas, onion, garlic, coriander, cumin, chili powder, parsley, salt, pepper, baking soda, and lemon juice in a food processor and pulse until finely chopped but not pureed; scrape down the sides of the bowl as necessary and add 1 to 2 tablespoons water if needed.

Heat 3 inches of oil in a large deep pot over medium-high heat to 350°F (the oil is ready when a pinch of the chickpea mixture begins sizzling immediately when added to it). Working in batches, scoop out heaping tablespoons of the mixture, shape them into balls or small patties, and fry, turning occasionally, until golden brown, 3 to 5 minutes. If the patties are brittle or if the mixture separates in the oil, stir the egg into the mixture and continue frying.

Serve the falafel in Pita Bread (page 151) with Tomato Sauce (page 71), shredded iceberg lettuce, and Pickled Onions (page 55). Pass Cucumber Sambal (page 65) on the side.

4 SERVINGS (MAKES 12 TO 16 PATTIES)

SPICY OKRA

People tend to either love or hate okra, which originated in Africa and spread to Arabia, Europe, the Caribbean, Brazil, India, and the United States. I happen to love it and think it adds great texture and color to meals, but I do remember being a little put off by its slimy texture the first time I had it. Once you get over that, it's easy to like. Look for pods that are uniform in color, with no discoloration or soft spots. Smaller pods are usually more tender than large pods.

1½ pounds okra, cut into 1-inch pieces
2 tablespoons peanut oil
2 medium red onions, sliced
4 tomatoes, chopped
2 bird's-eye chilies, seeds and ribs removed, chopped
½ cup peanuts, coarsely chopped
3 garlic cloves, minced
½ teaspoon salt, or to taste

Bring a medium saucepan of salted water to a boil. Add the okra and simmer until tender, about 5 minutes. Drain and pat dry.

Heat the oil in a large sauté pan over high heat. Add the onions, tomatoes, chilies, and peanuts and sauté, stirring frequently, until the onions are translucent, about 5 minutes. Reduce the heat to medium, add the garlic, and cook until golden, about 5 minutes. Stir in the okra and cook until heated through, about 2 minutes. Season with the salt.

4 TO 6 SERVINGS

metrorail
metrorail
metrorail
DTC 2190 C
SEA BREEZE
NIKKI

Barbecued Snapper

Cassava-Stuffed Shrimp

Chermoula-Roasted Bass

Char with Sakay

Curried Trout with Coconut-Chili Sauce

Simbujen, Dakar, Senegal

Fried Catfish

Lobster Skewers with Couscous-Avocado Salad

Malata

Oysters with Green Tomato Water

Rice-Crusted Hake

FISH AND SEAFOOD

Plantain-Crusted Yellowtail

Salmon Skewers with Tamarind Sauce

Seafood and Rice

Seared Cured Yellowtail

Shrimp Piri Piri

Snapper Wrapped in Banana Leaves

Spiced Bass with Crunchy Rice and Watercress Salad

Trout Spaghetti

Warm Tuna "Tartare"

Tomato-Roasted Shark

CHERMOULA-ROASTED BASS

A lot of people like flavorful food but they don't particularly care for spicy food. For these people, chermoula fits the bill—it serves up flavor without spiciness and is rich, floral, and flavorful without being overpoweringly hot, making it a great seasoning for bass or any other firm, white-fleshed fish.

In this recipe, I use two techniques to keep the fish moist. Cooking it on the bone helps to prevent the meat from drying out, while wrapping the fish in banana leaves—a technique that's used throughout West Africa—keeps it moist and intensifies the flavors.

2 tablespoons olive oil
One 3- to 4-pound sea bass, cleaned and scaled
Salt
½ cup Chermoula (page 15)
1 banana leaf (page 1) **or about a 4-foot length of parchment paper**
1 lemon, thinly sliced
3 garlic cloves, cut in half
1 lemon, quartered, plus lemon wedges for serving

Preheat the oven to 350°F. Brush a baking sheet with the olive oil. Make 3 deep diagonal slashes, all the way to the bone, in each side of the fish. Generously sprinkle salt on each side and in the cavity, then brush both sides of the fish and the cavity with the chermoula.

Lay the banana leaf or a 4-foot length of parchment paper on a work surface, and lay the fish across the leaf, about 2 inches from one short end. Arrange the lemon slices and garlic cloves over the fish. Squeeze the juice from the lemon quarters over it. Fold the end of the banana leaf or parchment over the top of the fish, fold the sides in, then wrap the rest of the leaf or parchment around the fish. Tie the packet around the middle and at the ends with kitchen string. Place on the baking sheet.

Roast for 40 minutes, or until the fish is cooked through. Carefully unwrap the fish to check for doneness; the flesh should be opaque and just flaky.

Transfer to a platter, garnish with Preserved Citrus Peel (page 59), and serve with lemon wedges and garlic.

4 SERVINGS

CHAR WITH SAKAY

About 100 miles south of Cape Town, the cold waters of the Atlantic meet the tropical waters of the Indian Ocean, giving the Cape fishermen an extraordinary range of fish to haul back to shore. A fish they called salmon-trout was surprisingly familiar to me—it's very similar to char, a fish I was raised with in Sweden that has become increasingly available in the United States over the last decade. Char is a pink-fleshed fish that culinarily is a cross between salmon and trout, and it thrives in icy cold water. It's excellent baked, broiled, fried, grilled, poached, or steamed. Here the fish is kept moist by cooking it at low heat with sakay, the hot and spicy rub from Madagascar that is at home on tables around the world. If char is not available, substitute salmon fillets.

Eight 3-ounce skinless char fillets
2 cups olive oil
2 cloves garlic, minced
2 teaspoons chopped thyme
1 cup Sakay (page 61)
1 lime, quartered

Place the char in a shallow pan. Combine the olive oil, garlic, and thyme and pour over the char, turning to coat. Cover and refrigerate for 2 hours.

Preheat the oven to 275°F. Remove the fish from the marinade and rub all over with the sakay. Transfer to a baking pan that holds the fish comfortably, and bake for 20 minutes.

Remove from the oven and let the fish rest in the pan for 10 minutes to cool slightly.

Squeeze a lime quarter over each fillet, and serve with Cucumber Sambal (page 65) and Mango Couscous (page 96).

4 SERVINGS

CURRIED TROUT WITH COCONUT-CHILI SAUCE

British colonial settlers brought their love of fishing with them, and these devoted anglers stocked the highland rivers of East Africa with trout so they could fly-fish in their spare time. Trout is now abundant in the rivers of Uganda, Kenya, and Tanzania, and has become an important food in inland areas. I use it in this recipe, which was inspired by Kenya's samaki wa kupaka (literally, "grilled fish"), a traditional preparation of fish with coconut sauce and chilies. The overriding flavor of this dish comes from the coconut-chili sauce, which is not a sauce in the traditional French way, where butter or oil is added. African-style cooking is much more organic and natural, and this sauce is the perfect example—it's refreshing, with lots of great flavor.

Two 1½-pound trout, cleaned
Salt
¼ cup Green Curry Paste (page 26) **or Thai curry paste**
3 tablespoons peanut oil
1 serrano chili, seeds and ribs removed, minced
2 tomatoes, roughly chopped, or 1 cup chopped canned tomatoes
1 small red onion, diced
1 garlic clove, minced
1 cup coconut milk
Juice of 2 lemons
Lemon wedges

Preheat the oven to 375°F. Lightly grease a baking dish large enough to hold the fish comfortably. Make 3 diagonal slashes about ¼ inch deep in both sides of each fish. Season on both sides with salt. Combine the curry paste and peanut oil in a small bowl. Generously brush half the mixture on both sides and in the cavity of each fish. Place the fish in the baking dish.

Roast the fish, turning once, until the flesh is opaque and just beginning to flake, about 8 to 10 minutes on each side.

While the fish is roasting, combine the remaining curry paste mixture, the chili, tomatoes, onion, and garlic in a saucepan. Bring to a simmer over low heat and simmer until the sauce is slightly reduced, about 10 minutes. Add the coconut milk and simmer for another 10 minutes. Season with 1 teaspoon salt, and pour into a small serving bowl.

Remove the fish from the oven and drizzle with the lemon juice, then cover loosely with aluminum foil and let rest for 5 minutes. Arrange the fish on a platter and garnish with lemon wedges. Pass the sauce on the side, and serve with Yellow Rice (page 105).

4 SERVINGS

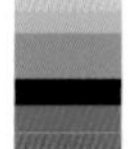

My most vivid memories of Dakar revolve around the sea.

THE SENEGALESE CAPITAL, DAKAR, is the westernmost point of Africa, sitting on a peninsula that juts into the Atlantic Ocean. Given its location, it's no surprise that the most vivid memories of my visit there revolve around the sea.

My time in Dakar was short, so I was lucky to have two guides—Abdullah, the nephew of a friend from New York, and his twenty-six-year-old aunt, Aminata—to show me around. Knowing I was interested in food, they took me to markets around the city. Late one sunny afternoon we set off for Simbujen, the beachfront fish market where returning fishermen unload and sell their daily catch. It was a magical day that gave me an upfront glimpse into day-to-day life in Dakar.

To get to the market, we walked along the edge of a cliff overlooking the Atlantic Ocean. Vans—so overloaded that the back doors were left open to accommodate more passengers—whizzed past us on the busy street. Down below on Koussoum Beach, swarms of men were exercising, jogging, or doing calisthenics in unison on the sand. "They do this every day before and after work, all year long," Abdullah explained. I contrasted the image of the dozens of men on the sunlit beach below me with thoughts of my friends in New York, who race to the gym to hit the treadmill after work every day, and thought that this is just one example of how the Senegalese have gotten life right.

A brightly colored fishing boat skimmed along the surface of the Atlantic Ocean to land on the beach as we approached Simbujen. My first sight of the market was a neat row of to be sold at market the next day. She was truly a woman in charge of the situation, not a sight I saw often in the male-dominated society of Senegal.

Beyond the ocean, Dakar is a most impressive place. It's a city of French influences, and as I strolled through the old town—with its tree-lined avenues, storefront cafés, and terra-cotta rooftops—I often had to remind myself that I was in Africa and not southern France. In the newer parts of the city, however, there was no need to remind myself of where I was—it's unmistakably African. Dakar is a chaotic city of people on the go, and everywhere I went, it seemed like everyone had something to sell: vendors rush through the streets, knocking on taxi windows to sell everything from candies, toothbrushes, tissues, basketballs, and sandals to manicure sets, television antennas, bathroom scales, and bags of garlic. Music was everywhere, and to me it seemed like the city has its own soundtrack. Senegalese music is perhaps the most famous of the entire continent, and no visit to Dakar is complete without a visit to one of the many downtown clubs—including Thiossane, the nightclub run by the legendary Senegalese singer, songwriter, and composer Youssou N'Dour—where live music is performed nightly.

Like many of the other places I visited in Africa, Dakar struck me as a city that embraced its traditions while moving into the twenty-first century. I've read that it's believed the name Dakar is derived from the Wolof tribe's word for refuge. I can't think of a more apt name for this city of beautiful sights and gracious people.

MALATA

The waters that surround Mozambique offer an overwhelming range of fresh seafood, including incredible clams that are the centerpiece of malata, a seafood stew that showcases a number of typical African ingredients: peanuts, pumpkin, pumpkin leaves, and chilies. In Mozambique, this dish would often be made with canned or dried clams, but here I call for fresh clams, which give a wonderful briny taste, and substitute spinach for the hard-to-find pumpkin leaves.

⅓ cup peanut oil
1 cup peanuts
1 pound butternut squash, seeded and cut into 1-inch dice
1 medium Spanish onion, diced
4 garlic cloves, minced
4 bird's-eye chilies, seeds and ribs removed, finely chopped
One 3-inch piece ginger, peeled and minced
4 dozen littleneck clams, scrubbed
½ cup bottled clam juice
½ cup dry white wine
2 teaspoons chopped thyme
½ teaspoon salt
4 cups coarsely chopped spinach
2 limes, quartered

Heat the peanut oil in a large sauté pan over high heat. When the oil shimmers, add the peanuts, butternut squash, onion, and garlic and sauté until the onion is translucent, about 10 minutes. Stir in the chilies and ginger and cook, stirring occasionally, for 10 minutes.

Add the clams, clam juice, white wine, thyme, and salt, cover, and cook until the clams open, about 10 minutes. As the clams open, transfer them to a large bowl. Discard any unopened clams.

Add the spinach to the sauté pan, cover, and cook until the spinach has wilted, 2 to 3 minutes. Return the clams to the pan to warm them through.

Divide the malata among four warmed serving bowls and serve with the lime wedges.

4 SERVINGS

OYSTERS WITH GREEN TOMATO WATER

I set off for Africa expecting to find basic, poor man's cooking, but as I traveled throughout the continent, the variety and depth of the food I found forced me to rethink my assumptions. From street food to casual cafés and high-end restaurants, there was a remarkable respect for ingredients that I hadn't expected. This recipe was inspired by a meal I had at Le Quartier Français in the town of Franschhoek, nestled in a Cape Wineland valley settled by French Huguenots. The young Dutch chef, Margot Janse, is creating incredibly avant-garde food that mixes cultures and ingredients in the most elegant way. I make this with Kumumoto oysters, which are my favorite, but you can use whatever type you prefer.

½ seedless (English) cucumber, chopped
1 beefsteak or large globe tomato, roughly chopped
1 tomatillo, husked, rinsed, and roughly chopped, or 1 small green tomato, roughly chopped
1 small garlic clove, minced
½ jalapeño chili, seeds and ribs removed, chopped
One 1-inch piece ginger, peeled and coarsely chopped
1 teaspoon chopped cilantro
Juice of 1 lime
Salt
16 oysters, scrubbed
1 teaspoon chili oil

Combine the cucumber, tomato, tomatillo, garlic, jalapeño, ginger, and cilantro in a blender and puree until smooth. Strain the puree through a fine-mesh strainer lined with cheesecloth into a bowl. Reserve the liquid and transfer the thick pulp that remains in the cheesecloth to a separate bowl. Stir in the lime juice, season with salt, and set aside.

Just before serving, shuck the oysters; leave them in their bottom shells, but gently loosen them from the shells. Top each oyster with a drop of chili oil, ½ teaspoon of the tomato pulp, and 1½ teaspoons of the tomato liquid.

4 SERVINGS AS AN APPETIZER

RICE-CRUSTED HAKE

One of my philosophies as a chef is to use ordinary foods in different, unusual ways. One day, I looked into the pantry and thought, "How can I create a crust with something as simple as plain, ordinary white rice?" My creation—essentially, ground raw rice—is something I've since used over and over to make a delicious and original coating for fried fish fillets.

If you can't find rice flour at your local market, you can make it just by grinding 1 cup of uncooked rice in a food processor on low speed until powdery. Hake is available throughout Africa, but if you have trouble finding it, you can substitute cod, which is similar in taste and texture and much more widely available in the United States.

1½ teaspoons ground ginger
Seeds from 4 green cardamom pods
1 teaspoon ground coriander
1 cup rice flour (see headnote)
1 teaspoon salt
1 teaspoon freshly ground black pepper
½ cup cornstarch
4 egg whites
Twelve 3-ounce skinless hake or cod fillets
½ cup olive oil
Two 3-inch pieces ginger, peeled and grated
2 lemons, quartered

Toast the ginger, cardamom, and coriander in a small sauté pan over low heat until fragrant, 30 to 60 seconds. Set aside to cool.

Combine the toasted spices with the rice flour, salt, pepper, and cornstarch and spread on a plate. Whisk the egg whites together in a shallow bowl. One at a time, dredge each fillet in the rice flour mixture, turning to coat on both sides, then dip in the egg whites, and coat again in the spiced rice mixture. Put the coated fillets on a plate.

Heat the oil in a large sauté pan over medium heat. Add the ginger and cook, stirring constantly, until fragrant, about 1 to 2 minutes. Working in batches, sear the fillets, turning once, until golden brown and crispy, about 4 minutes on each side.

Serve with Pistachio Rouille (page 57) and the lemon wedges.

6 SERVINGS

PLANTAIN-CRUSTED YELLOWTAIL

Plantains are used in all aspects of African meals, both savory and sweet. Here I use them to make a flavorful crust for yellowtail, one of my all-time favorite fish. I'd always associated yellowtail with Japanese cooking, so I was surprised to see it on the menu in Cape Town and to learn that it is originally from the waters off California and Mexico.

3 tablespoons Mango Sambal (page 64)
1 teaspoon curry powder
2 green plantains
Four 6-ounce yellowtail or tuna steaks
Salt
3 tablespoons olive oil

Combine the sambal and curry powder in a blender and puree until smooth, adding 1 to 2 teaspoons of water—no more—if necessary. Set aside.

Peel the plantains (see page 5) and slice them as thin as possible on a mandoline or with a vegetable peeler. (It's not possible to slice them thin enough with a knife.) Lay the fish on a work surface and season with salt. Brush with the mango-curry mixture. Arrange the plantain slices on top of the fish, overlapping them slightly to completely cover the surface of each steak; press down lightly with your fingers so they stick to the fish.

Heat the olive oil in a large nonstick sauté pan over high heat. Carefully add the fish, plantain side down, reduce the heat to medium, and cook for 7 minutes. Flip the fish and cook for 30 seconds.

Serve with Yellow Rice (page 105) and Creamed Swiss Chard (page 177).

4 SERVINGS

SALMON SKEWERS WITH TAMARIND SAUCE

I am always on the lookout for new recipes and ingredients, and everyone I meet becomes a source of information and inspiration. My friend Kingsley's mother was the muse for this recipe: during one of her annual visits to New York, she invited me over for a lavish Saint Lucian feast, including a dish made with tamarind. It reminded me how much I love this tart, lip-puckering fruit, which I use here as a complement to rich and oily salmon.

To ensure the skewers don't stick, make sure the grill grate is hot first. You'll know the fish is cooked through when the salmon flesh easily releases from the grill without sticking.

½ cup peanut oil
2 pounds salmon fillet, cut into 2-inch cubes
¼ cup olive oil
1 medium yellow onion, roughly chopped
1 garlic clove, minced
1 tablespoon curry powder
1 cup white wine vinegar
¼ cup dry red wine
1 tablespoon cornstarch
2 tablespoons tamarind paste (see page 5–6)
2 teaspoons sugar
½ teaspoon salt

Pour the peanut oil into a medium bowl, add the salmon, and turn to coat. Set fish aside for 30 minutes. Soak 16 bamboo skewers in water for at least 30 minutes. Prepare a medium-hot grill fire.

While the salmon is sitting in the peanut oil, heat the olive oil in a large sauté pan over medium heat. Add the onion and garlic and sauté until onion is translucent, about 5 minutes. Stir in the curry powder, vinegar, red wine, cornstarch, tamarind paste, and sugar and bring to a simmer. Reduce the heat to low and simmer for 5 minutes, or until the sauce thickens slightly. Remove from the heat and let cool slightly, then transfer to a blender and puree until smooth. Transfer 1 cup to a small serving bowl and set aside. Reserve the remaining sauce for basting the salmon.

Sprinkle the salmon with the salt and thread onto the skewers. Arrange on the grill and cook for 3 to 4 minutes on each side, or just until cooked through, brushing frequently with the tamarind sauce.

Serve with Cumin Braii Bread (page 141), Almond Sambal (page 65), and the bowl of reserved sauce.

6 TO 8 SERVINGS

SEAFOOD AND RICE

Chep bu jen—literally, fish and rice—is served at every special occasion in Senegal. It can be a relatively humble dish, made with inexpensive types of fish, or it can be more luxurious, like this version, which is a hybrid of chep bu jen and the seafood paellas of Spain.

In Senegal, it is made with broken jasmine rice. Broken jasmine rice is not widely available in the United States, but you'll get fine results with regular jasmine or any other long-grain rice. I like to serve it as a family-style meal while entertaining, which is very much in keeping with the spirit of African dining.

5 tablespoons olive oil, divided
3 garlic cloves, cut in half
2 shallots, minced
2 serrano chilies, seeds and ribs removed, finely chopped
8 littleneck clams, scrubbed
3 cups chicken stock
½ cup white wine
8 mussels, scrubbed and debearded
1 cup jasmine or other long-grain white rice
One 2-inch piece ginger, peeled and minced
1 teaspoon coriander seeds
1 bay leaf
2 sprigs thyme
3 tomatoes, diced, or 1½ cups chopped canned tomatoes
1 tablespoon tomato paste
1 tablespoon mild chili powder
Salt
Four 3-ounce skin-on black bass fillets
8 jumbo shrimp, preferably head-on, cut into 3 pieces each (in the shell)
Juice of 2 limes
2 sprigs cilantro, chopped
1 lemon, quartered

Heat 3 tablespoons of the olive oil in a Dutch oven or other large pot over medium heat. Add the garlic, shallots, and chilies, and sauté until soft. Add the clams and cook for 2 minutes, stirring constantly. Add the chicken stock and wine, bring to a simmer, and simmer for 3 minutes. Add the mussels, cover, and cook until the mussels and clams open up. Transfer the clams and mussels to a bowl; discard any unopened shellfish. Strain the liquid and set aside.

Wipe out the pot, add 1 tablespoon olive oil, and heat over medium heat. Add the rice, ginger, coriander seeds, bay leaf, thyme, tomatoes, tomato paste, chili powder, and 1 teaspoon salt and cook, stirring, for 3 minutes. Add the reserved cooking liquid, cover, and bring to a boil. Reduce the heat and simmer for 10 minutes. Remove from the heat and let sit, covered, for 15 minutes, or until all the liquid is absorbed.

Meanwhile, heat the remaining tablespoon of olive oil in a large sauté pan over medium heat. Season the bass on both sides with salt, add to the pan, skin side down, and sear for 2 minutes. Turn and sear on the other side for another 2 minutes. Transfer to a plate. Add the shrimp to the pan and sauté for 30 to 60 seconds, or until the shells turn bright red. Transfer to a separate plate and sprinkle with about ¼ teaspoon salt.

Stir the lime juice, cilantro, and ½ teaspoon salt into the rice. Fold in the mussels, clams, and shrimp. Remove the bay leaf. Arrange the bass fillets and lemon wedges on top of the rice, and serve directly from the pot, with toasted baguette slices.

4 SERVINGS

SEARED CURED YELLOWTAIL

While visiting the Cape Winelands, I spent one afternoon at the region's annual wine and cheese festival. From the music to the blond, blue-eyed people, the Dutch influence lives on in South African wine country. A lot of the foods I saw on my travels there were similar to the northern European foods I'd grown up with: cheese, sausage, and smoked and cured fish. This recipe gives an African slant to the classic northern European cured salmon, replacing the salmon with yellowtail and the dill with African spices. Because you do not cook cured fish through, it's important to use sushi-quality yellowtail so you are certain to get the freshest available fish. It can be challenging to find yellowtail; if it is not available, substitute an equal amount of tuna.

2 cups sugar
1 cup salt
4 cilantro sprigs, chopped
2 chives
½ cup Ras al-Hanout (page 32), divided
2 garlic cloves, minced
2 serrano chilies, seeds and ribs removed, finely chopped
One 3-inch piece ginger, peeled and roughly chopped
One 3-inch piece horseradish, peeled and roughly chopped
2 pounds sushi-quality yellowtail or tuna
1 tablespoon olive oil

Combine the sugar, salt, cilantro, chives, 2 tablespoons of the ras al-hanout, the garlic, chilies, ginger, and horseradish. Generously rub the yellowtail with the mixture. Put the yellowtail in a deep container and spoon the remaining sugar-spice blend over it. Cover and refrigerate for 6 hours. (As the fish cures, the curing mixture will become liquid.)

Remove the fish and pat dry (discard the curing liquid). Dust the fish with the remaining 6 tablespoons ras al-hanout.

Heat the oil in a large sauté pan over high heat. When the oil shimmers, add the fish and sear for 30 seconds on each side. Remove from the pan and slice into ¼-inch-thick pieces.

Serve with Preserved Citrus Peel (page 59).

8 TO 10 SERVINGS AS AN APPETIZER

SHRIMP PIRI PIRI

Piri piri, the national dish of Mozambique, was one of the first African foods I tried when I was cooking in Europe. After the first bite I could see why it's so popular, not only in Mozambique but also throughout the southern regions of Africa and in Brazilian and Portuguese cooking. In Mozambique, piri piri is typically served with rice to cut the spiciness. I use Bibb lettuce, which takes away some of the heat for a very well-balanced dish.

12 jumbo shrimp, peeled and deveined
½ cup plus 2 tablespoons Piri Piri (page 56), **divided**
2 tablespoons olive oil
½ teaspoon salt
1 lime, quartered
12 Bibb lettuce leaves

Toss the shrimp with ½ cup of the piri piri in a large bowl. Refrigerate for 20 minutes.

Heat the olive oil in a large sauté pan over medium heat. Add the shrimp and cook for 2 minutes on each side, or until opaque throughout. Transfer to a plate and sprinkle with the salt. Squeeze the lime quarters over the shrimp.

Spread ½ teaspoon of the remaining piri piri sauce on each lettuce leaf. Place a shrimp on each leaf and fold over bottom and sides to form a wrap. Serve immediately.

4 SERVINGS AS AN APPETIZER

SNAPPER WRAPPED IN BANANA LEAVES

Cooking food in banana leaves is a tradition in West Africa, where much cooking is still done outdoors on a three-stone hearth. This recipe, a one-pot dinner, gently poaches tender snapper in a sweet, rich coconut-milk broth.

2 jalapeño chilies, seeds and ribs removed, finely chopped
One 3-inch piece ginger, peeled and cut into ¼-inch dice
4 garlic cloves, minced
2 sprigs cilantro, chopped
1 teaspoon cayenne pepper
3 tablespoons olive oil
Six 6-ounce skin-on snapper fillets
2 to 3 banana leaves, cut into six 8 x 12-inch sheets
1 lemon, sliced and seeded
1 tomato, sliced
1 medium Spanish onion, finely diced
1½ cups long-grain white rice
3 cups chicken stock
One 15-ounce can coconut milk
2 teaspoons salt
2 cups trimmed morning glory or trimmed spinach
2 yellow plantains, peeled and cut into ½-inch slices

Mix the jalapeños, ginger, garlic, cilantro, cayenne pepper, and 2 tablespoons of the olive oil in a small bowl. Place 1 snapper fillet skin side up in the center of a banana leaf and brush or spoon one-sixth of the jalapeño mixture over the fish. Place a lemon slice and a tomato slice in the center of the fillet. Fold the sides of the leaf in over the fish to make a neat packet, and tie the packet with kitchen string. Repeat with the remaining fillets.

Combine the remaining tablespoon of olive oil with the onion, rice, chicken stock, coconut milk, and salt in a Dutch oven or other large deep pot and bring to a boil over medium-high heat. Reduce the heat to a simmer, cover, and cook for 5 minutes.

Carefully arrange the fish packets and plantains on top of the rice and simmer, uncovered, for 10 minutes. Cover and simmer for 10 minutes. Remove from the heat and let stand, covered, for 5 to 10 minutes, until the rice absorbs most of the liquid.

Transfer the packets to a plate to drain. Stir the morning glory into the rice, cover, and let sit for 3 minutes, or until the leaves are wilted.

For a striking presentation, serve the fish still wrapped in the banana leaves for guests to unwrap. For a less dramatic, but less messy, option, unwrap the packets and transfer the fish to a platter or individual plates. Serve with the rice and plantains.

6 SERVINGS

TROUT SPAGHETTI

Apart from the brief Italian occupation starting in 1936, Ethiopia has never been ruled by a foreign power. Ethiopian resistance forces and British troops pushed out the Italian army, but these foreign invaders did leave one lasting impact—the only non-Ethiopian food I saw in Addis Ababa was Italian. I was delighted to visit one of these Italian restaurants because, after days of eating nothing but meat and lamb stews with injera, this refreshing pasta dish provided a welcome change.

½ cup olive oil, divided
1 tablespoon chopped mint
Juice of 2 limes
2 tablespoons Berbere (page 12) **or chili powder, divided**
Three 1-pound skinless rainbow trout fillets, cut on the diagonal into ¼-inch slices
3 tablespoons Spiced Butter (page 34) **or unsalted butter**
1 medium red onion, roughly chopped
1 pound spaghetti
2 garlic cloves, minced
1 teaspoon salt
2 basil leaves, chopped
Fresh Cheese with Chives (page 52)

Combine ¼ cup of the olive oil, the mint, lime juice, and 1 tablespoon of the berbere in a medium bowl. Add the trout and turn to coat. Cover and refrigerate to cure for 2 hours.

Put a large pot of salted water on to boil. Drain the trout and pat dry. Set aside.

Combine the butter, the remaining ¼ cup olive oil, the remaining 1 tablespoon berbere, and the red onion in a sauté pan large enough to accommodate the cooked pasta and the sauce and sauté until the onion is aromatic and softened, about 10 minutes.

Meanwhile, drop the pasta into the boiling water and cook until al dente; drain.

Two to 3 minutes before the pasta is done, add the garlic to the onion and cook over low heat until golden. Stir in the salt.

Add the pasta to the sauce. Turn the heat to medium and, using tongs, toss the pasta with the sauce for a minute, then pull the pan from the heat. Fold in the basil and cured trout, and serve immediately. Spoon dollops of the fresh cheese over the pasta.

4 SERVINGS

TOMATO-ROASTED SHARK

The life of a fisherman is a dangerous one, as I learned during my stay in Cape Town. One morning, I got up early to watch the fishermen set off from Kalk Bay. I arrived late and was disappointed to have missed most of the boats, but as it turned out, I didn't miss out on any excitement. As I walked along the empty piers, I met an old fisherman with an extraordinary tale to tell: he'd been a fisherman all his life, but he swore that he would never go out to sea again, because the previous night a vicious great white shark had attacked his boat, jumping over the prow to attack. It just missed him by a few inches. The experience was so terrifying that nothing, he said, would entice him to fish again. He may have been telling a tall tale but I chose to believe it, and to this day I think of his story every time I see shark meat at the fish market.

⅓ cup plus ¼ cup olive oil, divided
8 tomatoes, quartered
1½ teaspoons sugar
½ cup roughly chopped blanched almonds
¾ cup red wine vinegar
3 garlic cloves, minced
1 shallot, minced
One 3-inch piece ginger, peeled and grated
2 basil leaves
Juice of 2 lemons
½ cup white wine vinegar
1½ teaspoons salt
Four 8-ounce mako shark fillets

Preheat the oven to 300°F. Brush a baking sheet with 2 tablespoons of the olive oil. Toss the tomatoes with the sugar and arrange skin side down on the pan. Roast for 40 minutes.

Sprinkle the tomatoes with the almonds and roast for an additional 25 minutes.

While the tomatoes are roasting, combine the red wine vinegar, garlic, shallot, ginger, basil, lemon juice, ⅓ cup olive oil, the white wine vinegar, and salt in a deep skillet and bring to a boil. Reduce the heat to low, add the shark, and simmer for 5 minutes. Remove from the heat, cover, and let stand for 10 minutes.

Raise the oven temperature to 350°F. Brush a rimmed baking sheet with the remaining 2 tablespoons olive oil. Using a slotted spoon, transfer the shark to the baking sheet; reserve ¼ cup of the poaching liquid. Season with salt, then carefully spoon the tomatoes and almonds over the shark. Roast for 7 minutes, or until the shark is firm.

Arrange the shark on a platter and drizzle with the reserved poaching liquid. Serve with Yellow Rice (page 105).

4 SERVINGS

How to Truss a Chicken or Other Bird

How to Cut Up a Chicken

Chicken Mofongo

Chicken Stew (Doro Wett)

Duck Skewers

Addis Ababa, Ethiopia

Dark-Spiced Turkey Legs

POULTRY

Egyptian-Style Salted Squab

Foie Gras–Date Chutney with Toasted Spiced Dried Fruit Bread

Guinea Hen with Shiro

Harissa-Roasted Turkey Breast

Jerk Chicken

Lemon-Olive Chicken

Moroccan-Style Duck Breasts

Jollof Rice

AS I TRAVELED THROUGH AFRICA, there was one sight that quickly became familiar to me: roaming chickens pecking at the ground for a morsel of food. Whether I was in the city or a rural village, I soon grew accustomed to sharing the walkway with a mother hen and her chicks.

Chicken is an affordable luxury in Africa: they cost little to raise; you can eat the entire bird, so there's no waste; and they produce eggs, which provide another source of food. Many families raise their own chickens and allow them to wander the surrounding areas in search of food. Because they are allowed to forage, the meat of these chickens is stringy and tough, but home cooks accommodate for this shortcoming in the most delicious ways. Stews like Ethiopia's doro wett, Senegal's chicken yassa, or Morocco's chicken tagine are slow-cooked for hours to produce tender, succulent, flavorful meat. Intense flavoring also helps to mask the quality of the bird—case in point is Mozambique's national dish, chicken piri piri, which is so blisteringly hot it can set your mouth on fire.

Even for people who don't raise their own chickens, preparation is completely different in Africa. In most places, chicken doesn't come in tightly wrapped plastic packages at the supermarket: they are sold live at the market and taken home to be butchered. But although it is bought on the dirty street in total chaos, when the chicken comes

home it's a different story, with food safety not taken lightly. Once butchered, chicken parts are meticulously soaked in water, then rubbed all over with lemons.

Chicken, of course, is not the only bird served at African tables. Game birds like guinea fowl are popular in South Africa, where there is a long and respected hunting tradition. Up in the north, pigeon is a big favorite. Nowhere is pigeon more appreciated than in Egypt—young squab is such a delicacy that pigeon nesting is encouraged everywhere and its meat is featured in a number of beloved traditional recipes.

As I ate my way through Africa, I realized there is an essential difference between African cooking and the European and American approach. African cooking is much looser and unstructured. You could never substitute chicken for beef in steak frites, or lamb for chicken in fried chicken, for example, but in Africa the meat often serves as the canvas for the dish, and it's the preparation that is the essential component—for instance, I had both fish and chicken yassa, and tagines are prepared with chicken as regularly as they are with lamb.

In this chapter, I've collected a number of traditional poultry recipes as well as newly created dishes inspired by my travels to help bring a taste of Africa to your table.

HOW TO TRUSS A CHICKEN OR OTHER BIRD

When you are cooking a whole chicken or other bird, I recommend trussing—tying the bird together with string—to help it maintain its shape during cooking and make it easier to carve. It's a simple technique that takes only a minute or two, and the results are worth the effort.

1. Cut a long piece of kitchen twine—about 2½ to 3 feet for a chicken. Place the chicken (or other bird) breast side up on the work surface, with the drumsticks toward you, and slide the center of the string under the tail end of the chicken.

2. Pull the ends of the string up and cross them over the drumsticks, then run the left end of the string under the right drumstick and the right end under the left drumstick and pull to bring the drumsticks together.

3. Bring both ends of the twine across the breasts and over the wings. Cross the ends over at the neck end. Place your hand over the strings at the neck to keep them in place, turn the bird over, and pull the string taut around the chicken and over the wings, then tie into a knot. Tuck the end of each wing under the back of the chicken so they stay in place.

HOW TO CUT UP A CHICKEN

Cutting up a chicken is a skill I think everyone should know. Some people get intimidated by the thought of cutting through the bones, but it's easy to do—and as an added bonus, it's cheaper to cut it up yourself rather than buying chicken that's already cut up. All you need is a sharp chef's knife and a cutting board. The technique that follows yields 10 pieces: 4 split breasts, 2 thighs, 2 legs, and 2 wings. Most recipes do not call for the wings, so you can either discard them or freeze them and then, when you have enough, use them to make stock.

1. Remove the neck and giblets and rinse the chicken under cold running water. Pat the chicken dry and place it breast side up on a cutting board.

2. Gently pull one of the legs away from the body and cut through the flap of skin between the thigh and the body. Holding the leg in one hand, bend the leg back until the bone snaps out of the joint. Hold the chicken firmly against the cutting board, cut through the tendons and the skin between the body and thigh, and pull the leg away. Repeat with the other leg. To separate the thighs and drumsticks, locate the joint that connects them and firmly cut through it with the knife.

3. Pull one wing straight out from the body and cut through the joint where the wing joins the breast. Repeat with the other wing.

4. Turn the chicken breast side down. Using your knife or poultry shears, cut along both sides of the backbone to separate the ribs from the backbone. Snap the backbone away from the breast, and cut through the ribs to separate the breasts from the backbone.

5. To split the breast, cut down along either side of the breastbone, then cut straight down through the center bones to separate the breasts. Cut each breast crosswise in half, pressing firmly on the knife to cut through the bones.

CHICKEN MOFONGO

I kicked off my exploration of African cooking with a trip to the Bronx Terminal Market in New York City. After prowling the market for an hour and a half checking out smoked fish and meats, spices, pastries, and other African foods, I was so hungry I stopped for lunch at a nearby Puerto Rican diner. I ordered chicken mofongo, a hearty, filling stew of mashed plantains, chicken, and hot sauce that has its roots in the cooking of West Africa. It is the embodiment of the poor man's cooking you see throughout Africa and the Caribbean—filling, nourishing, and inexpensive.

Keep an eye on the cassava as it cooks and remove it from the heat as soon as it is tender; if it overcooks, the texture becomes somewhat gelatinous.

¼ cup fresh lemon juice
2 tablespoons Dark Spice Mix (page 18)
6 boneless chicken thighs, cut crosswise into 2-inch strips
1 medium cassava root, peeled, rinsed, and cut into 2-inch cubes
1 medium sweet potato, peeled and cut into 2-inch cubes
2 tablespoons peanut oil
2 medium red onions, chopped
4 garlic cloves, minced
2 Scotch bonnet chilies, seeds and ribs removed, finely chopped
2 scallions, trimmed and chopped
4 small parsley sprigs, leaves only, chopped

Whisk together the lemon juice and the spice mix in a shallow pan. Add the chicken, turning to coat, then cover and refrigerate for 2 hours. Remove the chicken from the liquid and pat dry.

Meanwhile, place the cassava in a bowl and rinse in cold water until the water runs clear. Drain.

When ready to finish the dish, combine the cassava and sweet potato in a pot, cover with salted water, bring to a boil, and boil for 25 minutes, or until tender but not mushy. Drain, then transfer to a large bowl and mash with a fork to a chunky consistency.

While the cassava and sweet potatoes are cooking, heat the peanut oil in a large sauté pan over high heat. Add the onions and chicken strips and sauté for 5 minutes, stirring frequently, until the onions are translucent and the chicken is browned. Add the garlic and chilies and cook for another 10 minutes, or until the chicken is cooked through. Remove the pan from the heat and stir in the scallions and parsley.

Fold the chicken into the cassava–sweet potato mash. Serve warm, with Sautéed Morning Glory (page 192) and Tomato Sauce (page 71).

Note: For a more elegant presentation, pack each serving of mofongo into a lightly oiled ramekin or cup, then unmold onto a serving plate.

4 TO 6 SERVINGS

CHICKEN STEW (DORO WETT)

When I take people out for Ethiopian food for the first time, this chicken stew, called doro wett (also spelled as doro we't, doro wat, and doro wet), is a great introduction. It's the first Ethiopian dish I ever had, and I immediately liked the tender meat, the spicy eggs, and the flavorful sauce laced with berbere and ginger. It's a great dish to make for people who haven't eaten African food before because it's easy to understand and like.

Don't be alarmed when the sauce doesn't bind together and thicken like a traditional European-style sauce—it should in fact be liquidy and broken to soak into the injera it is served on.

2 medium red onions, diced
Salt
¼ cup Spiced Butter (page 34) **or 4 tablespoons (½ stick) unsalted butter, divided**
¼ teaspoon ground cardamom, preferably freshly ground
¼ teaspoon freshly ground black pepper
3 cloves
2 garlic cloves, finely chopped
One 1½-inch piece ginger, peeled and chopped
1 tablespoon Berbere (page 12) **or chili powder**
2½ cups chicken stock, divided
One 4- to 5-pound chicken, cut into 10 pieces (see page 242), **wings reserved for another use**
¼ cup dry red wine
Juice of 1 lime
2 hard-boiled eggs, peeled

Combine the onions, a pinch of salt, and half of the spiced butter in a Dutch oven or other large deep pot over low heat. Cook, stirring occasionally, until the onions are golden, about 15 minutes. Add the remaining butter, the cardamom, black pepper, cloves, garlic, ginger, and berbere and cook until the onions soften and take on the color of the spices, about 10 minutes.

Add 2 cups of the chicken stock and the chicken legs and thighs, bring to a simmer, and simmer for 15 minutes. Add the remaining ½ cup chicken stock and the wine, bring back to a simmer, and simmer for 10 minutes. Add the chicken breasts and simmer for 20 minutes.

Gently stir in the lime juice and eggs and simmer for another 5 minutes. The sauce will be loose and soupy. Season with salt to taste.

Serve with Lentil Stew (page 123).

6 SERVINGS

DUCK SKEWERS

Foods prepared on skewers are popular all over the world. Whether it's brochette in France or satay in Southeast Asia, I think skewering is a fun and easy way to serve meat. The inspiration for this dish came from my visit to the island of Zanzibar, where so many different worlds—Persian, Indian, Arabic, and African—have met over the centuries. These duck skewers are flavored with masala, a curry spice blend that Indian settlers brought to Zanzibar hundreds of years ago. They make an elegant appetizer and can be served right off the grill or at room temperature.

½ cup peanuts
½ cup Green Masala (page 27) **or curry powder**
Juice of 2 limes
1 teaspoon salt
4 boneless Pekin (Long Island) duck breasts
2 quinces or pears, peeled, cored, and cut into 2-inch chunks
2 medium red onions, cut into 2-inch chunks
8 scallions, white part only, cut crosswise in half
2 red bell peppers, cored, seeds and ribs removed, and cut into 2-inch squares

Soak 8 bamboo skewers in water for at least 30 minutes. Meanwhile, toast the peanuts in a small nonstick sauté pan over medium heat until golden, about 3 minutes. Transfer to a blender, add the masala, lime juice, and salt, and puree until smooth.

Score the skin of the duck breasts in a diamond pattern. Heat a large sauté pan over medium-high heat. Add the breasts, skin side down, and cook for 6 minutes to render the fat. Turn and cook for 2 minutes, but no longer—the meat should remain rare. Remove from the pan and allow to cool slightly, then cut each breast crosswise into 4 pieces.

Thread the duck, quinces, onions, scallions, and red peppers alternately onto the skewers, using 2 pieces of duck per skewer. Pour the peanut mixture into a wide shallow pan or baking dish. Add the skewers and turn to coat. Marinate for at least 15 minutes, and up to 2 hours.

Prepare a medium grill fire. If using a charcoal grill, bank the hot coals to either side. Place a drip pan beneath the cooking rack.

Arrange the skewers in the center of the grill and grill, turning frequently to avoid flare-ups, until the duck is medium-rare, about 7 to 10 minutes. If the marinade starts to burn, move the skewers to a cooler part of the grill. Transfer to a platter, tent with foil, and let rest for 5 minutes.

Serve with Vegetable Samosas (page 164).

4 SERVINGS (MAKES 8 SKEWERS)

I never imagined I'd be in a car with a live ram strapped to the top.

AS MY CAB LURCHED THROUGH THE STREETS of Addis Ababa, I reflected that I never imagined I'd be in a car with a live ram strapped to the top. But here I was, on my way to an Ethiopian cooking lesson , and the ram was a gift to my host. I couldn't have been more excited.

One of the first people I'd met in New York was Yeworkwoha "Workye" Ephrem, the chef-owner of Ghenet, an Ethiopian restaurant in New York City's NoLIta. Workye had arranged for her mother, Muluwork Asfaw, a master of traditional Ethiopian cooking, to give me a cooking lesson. Although she thought it was funny that a man would want to learn to cook—in Ethiopia, the kitchen is still a woman's domain—she was ready to teach me to make doro wett, the chicken stew that is Ethiopia's signature dish. When I arrived, I gave her the ram, which she tethered in the front yard among her chickens, and the lesson began.

I hadn't realized what an undertaking this lesson would be. Ethiopian dishes are made up of ingredients that are intensely flavored—and incredibly labor intensive to prepare. Berbere, the flavorful blend of dried chili peppers and spices used in nearly all Ethiopian dishes, takes days to make; instead of plain butter, Ethiopian cooking calls for a homemade spiced butter called nit'ir qibe. It is this layering of flavors that makes Ethiopian cooking so distinctive—and so delicious.

Everything was made from scratch. We started with the live chickens that roamed in the front yard, which we butchered, cleaned, and cured before cooking. I later learned just how important a step this was; it is said that before an Ethiopian girl marries, she must know the proper way to butcher a chicken for doro wett. As Mrs. Asfaw instructed me, she worked from memory without a recipe, adding a pinch of this and a dash of that to the simmering pots. Working side by side in her kitchen I remembered my Swedish grandmother, who taught me how to cook and would beam approval when I did something right, just as Mrs. Asfaw was doing.

Hours later, as the stew was finishing, guests began drifting in and out of the kitchen. Mealtimes are social events in Ethiopia, so nearly a dozen family members and neighbors had been invited to join us when we sat down to eat. The fruits of our daylong labor were arranged on a buffet, and the table was set with bottles of tej (honey wine), talla (the traditional home-brewed beer), and bottles of homemade liqueurs. In a traditional Ethiopian display of hospitality, Mrs. Asfaw went around the table, using a piece of injera to scoop up a bit of doro wett to feed each guest his or her first bite. We ate leisurely as we relaxed around the table. It was a very loving atmosphere—you could sense that everyone cherished Ethiopian culture and the country's past.

And that past is truly amazing. Once known as Abyssinia, Ethiopia is the land of Solomon and the Queen of Sheba. Some of the oldest churches in the world dot the mountainous landscapes, and three of the world's major religions—Judaism, Christianity, and Islam—have coexisted for centuries within Ethiopia's borders, blending to form a culture of tolerance and respect for differences.

Ethiopia is known as the land of thirteen months of sunshine. Most of the country is perched on a mile-high plateau; the rest ranges from a river gorge deeper and wider than the Grand Canyon to towering mountains reaching 15,000 feet above sea level, which kept out foreign invaders until the Italian occupation of 1936. As a result, Ethiopian culture and cuisine is largely undiluted by foreign influences. Ethiopians cherish this unadulterated way of life—in fact, the way Mrs. Asfaw taught me to prepare our feast is not far removed from the way those same dishes were prepared hundreds of years ago.

DARK-SPICED TURKEY LEGS

While European-style cooking usually relies on salt for flavor, African cooks look to spice blends to season poultry, meats, and fish. Featuring a deliciously subtle blend of citrus, spices, and ginger, these turkey legs are a sampler of some of my favorite African flavors prepared with European and American techniques and ingredients. First the turkey legs are rubbed with a spice mix, then they are cooked slowly in oil and butter—very much like a confit—to produce a richly flavored meat that's so tender it almost melts in your mouth.

3 tablespoons salt
4 cups orange juice
4 boneless turkey legs (about 1 pound each)
3 tablespoons Dark Spice Mix (page 18)
4 thyme sprigs, chopped
1 cup peanut oil, divided
1 cup Spiced Butter (page 34) **or ½ pound (2 sticks) unsalted butter**
One 3-inch piece ginger, peeled and grated

Combine the salt with 2 cups of the orange juice in a large bowl and stir to dissolve the salt. Add the turkey legs, cover, and refrigerate for at least 2 hours, but not more than 8.

Drain the turkey and pat dry. Combine the spice mix and thyme and rub generously over and under the turkey skin.

Heat 2 tablespoons of the peanut oil in a Dutch oven or other deep pot over medium heat. Add the turkey legs, in batches if necessary, and sear on all sides for about 4 minutes on each side. Reduce the heat to very low (return all the turkey to the pot), add the remaining 2 cups orange juice, the remaining ¾ cup plus 2 tablespoons oil, the butter, and ginger, and bring to a simmer. Simmer for 1½ hours, stirring occasionally.

Remove the turkey legs from the liquid with a slotted spoon (discard the liquid), and cut the legs in half. Serve with Quince Chutney (page 49).

6 TO 8 SERVINGS

EGYPTIAN-STYLE SALTED SQUAB

When most people think of Egypt, they probably think of the Pyramids. But when I think of Egypt, I think of one of the oldest markets in the world, the Khan el-Khalili, or, as it is more commonly known, the Khan. Located in the heart of Cairo, the Khan was built in 1382 as a hub of the spice trade. In fact, it is believed that the Khan was a hub of the Arab-dominated spice monopoly that led Europeans to seek new routes to the East—and ultimately led to Columbus's discovery of the Americas. This recipe is inspired by the still-vibrant market; however, shoppers at the Khan would probably make this with pigeon instead of squab, which is similar in taste and texture but much smaller in size.

½ cup salt
4 mint sprigs, leaves removed and chopped, stems reserved
Juice of 2 lemons
2 cups water
4 squab (about 1 pound each), each cut into 2 breast pieces and 2 whole legs (see page 242)
1 teaspoon ground cardamom, preferably freshly ground
1 teaspoon ground ginger
½ cup olive oil

Mix together the salt, mint leaves, lemon juice, and water in a bowl large enough to hold the squab pieces. Immerse the squab, weighting it down with a plate if necessary to keep it submerged. Cover and refrigerate for at least 2 hours, or as long as 8 hours.

Remove the squab from the brine and pat dry. Toss together the cardamom and ginger, and rub over the squab breasts.

Heat the olive oil over high heat in a sauté pan large enough to accommodate the squab. Add the squab legs and cook for 7 minutes, turning halfway through the cooking. Add the mint stems and the breasts, skin side down, and cook until the skin is crisp and deeply browned, 2 to 4 minutes. Turn the breasts and cook for another 2 minutes, until medium-rare. Transfer to a platter, tent with foil, and let rest for 5 minutes.

Serve with Pistachio Rouille (page 57) and Pickled Green and Yellow Papayas (page 54).

4 SERVINGS

FOIE GRAS–DATE CHUTNEY WITH TOASTED SPICED DRIED FRUIT BREAD

Most people wouldn't associate African cooking and luxury foods. However, Africa is a continent of extremes, where everything from the most humble grains and root vegetables to extravagant yellowtail and foie gras is served. I always associated foie gras with classic French cooking, so I was surprised to learn that the ancient Egyptians were the first to develop this sumptuous goose liver. In fact, a mural on a sarcophagus near the Memphis pyramids dating back to 2390 B.C. shows geese being forcibly fed pellets of grain to make the fatty livers that are now served at the finest restaurants around the world. This rich but simple appetizer highlights the ancient Egyptians' discovery of one of my all-time favorite foods.

8 ounces Grade A or B foie gras, cut into 1-inch cubes
Salt
1 shallot, minced
½ cup red wine vinegar
2 tarragon sprigs, leaves only, chopped
1 teaspoon ground coriander
1 teaspoon ground cumin
½ teaspoon ground cinnamon
One 3-inch piece ginger, peeled and grated
1 cup port
4 fresh figs, cut into 8 wedges each
8 pitted dates, diced
½ cup honey
Toasted Spiced Dried Fruit Bread (recipe follows)

Season the foie gras cubes lightly with salt. Heat a large sauté pan over high heat. Add the foie gras cubes and sear for about 30 seconds, shaking the pan constantly, until a golden brown crust is formed; be careful not to overcook. Transfer to a plate and set aside.

Add the shallot and a pinch of salt to the pan, reduce the heat to medium, and sauté until the shallot is softened, about 5 minutes. Add the red wine vinegar, tarragon, coriander, cumin, cinnamon, ginger, and port and cook, stirring often, to evaporate the alcohol, about 4 minutes. Add the figs and simmer for 10 minutes. Add the dates and honey and simmer for another 5 minutes. Season with salt, and set aside to cool.

Gently fold the foie gras into the date chutney, making sure to incorporate the juices left on the plate.

Serve with the spiced fruit bread.

6 SERVINGS AS AN APPETIZER

TOASTED SPICED DRIED FRUIT BREAD

4 tablespoons (½ stick) unsalted butter, softened
½ teaspoon ground ginger
½ teaspoon ground cardamom, preferably freshly ground
1 teaspoon ground cinnamon
2 teaspoons salt
6 slices Dried Fruit Bread (page 143)

Combine the softened butter with the ginger, cardamom, cinnamon, and salt. Spread the butter lightly on both sides of the fruit bread.

Heat a large skillet over medium heat. Working in batches, add the bread and fry, turning once, until golden brown, 1 to 2 minutes on each side. Serve warm.

GUINEA HEN WITH SHIRO

In Ethiopia, nearly every family keeps a supply of shiro powder on hand to make shiro wett, the hearty puree made of powdered dried chickpeas or yellow split peas. Since I discovered Ethiopian food after I moved to New York, shiro wett has become one of my favorite foods. It is commonly eaten on its own—religious Ethiopians observe hundreds of fast days a year, so vegetarian dishes are prepared frequently—or served as a side dish, but I like to stir it into stews, too. Here, I use shiro as the base for a guinea hen stew. In Ethiopia the guinea hen would be cooked on the bone, but I use diced, boneless meat for a quicker cooking time and more elegant presentation.

⅓ cup plus 2 tablespoons Spiced Butter (page 34) **or unsalted butter**

2 medium Spanish onions, diced

2 carrots, peeled and cut into 1-inch pieces

3 garlic cloves, minced

4 tomatoes, roughly chopped, or 2 cups canned chopped tomatoes

1 guinea hen, skin removed and discarded, meat removed and cut into 2-inch cubes; keep the white and dark meat separate

1½ cups shiro powder (see page 5)

6 cups chicken stock

2 cups 1-inch cubes peeled pumpkin or butternut squash

1 teaspoon salt

2 cups trimmed spinach

1 cup corn kernels (from 2 large ears)

Melt ⅓ cup of the butter in a large sauté pan over medium heat. Add the onions, carrots, garlic, and tomatoes and cook, stirring occasionally, until the onions are softened, about 20 minutes.

Add the dark meat, shiro powder, and chicken stock, bring to a simmer, stirring frequently, and simmer for 50 minutes.

About 10 minutes before the dark meat is done, heat the remaining 2 tablespoons butter in a wide sauté pan or wok over high heat. Add the pumpkin and stir-fry for 2 minutes, then add the white meat and salt and stir-fry for about another 6 minutes, shaking the pan and stirring constantly, until the meat is lightly browned and cooked through. Reduce the heat to low and stir in the spinach and corn. Cook until the spinach is wilted.

To serve, arrange the dark meat and shiro in the bottom of deep bowls and top with the white meat and vegetables.

4 SERVINGS

HARISSA-ROASTED TURKEY BREAST

Every year, my mother served turkey for Christmas, even though I always begged her to make goose instead because I thought turkey was too dry and bland. This recipe puts an end to all my objections to turkey—it's roasted with harissa, the fiery chili sauce that's a staple on every Tunisian table, so it's full of flavor, and it stays deliciously moist with crispy, crackling skin.

Unlike a traditional stuffing that is baked in the oven, the stuffing for this turkey is made on the stovetop—a convenience when the oven is filled with the roasting pan.

One 6-pound bone-in turkey breast (skin on)
Salt and freshly ground black pepper
4 garlic cloves
2 cinnamon sticks
½ medium yellow onion, finely chopped
1 cup Harissa (page 30)
Stuffing (recipe follows)

Preheat the oven to 400°F. Rinse the turkey under cold water and pat dry. Sprinkle on all sides with salt and pepper. Stuff the garlic cloves, cinnamon sticks, and onion into the neck cavity, and seal it closed with a wooden skewer or toothpick. Generously rub the harissa over and under the skin.

Place the turkey breast skin side up on a roasting rack in a roasting pan and cover with foil. Roast, basting occasionally with the juices that accumulate in the bottom of the pan, until an instant-read thermometer inserted into thickest part of the breast reads 160°F and the juices run clear, about 1½ hours. During the last 20 minutes of cooking remove the foil to brown the skin. Let the turkey rest for at least 20 minutes before carving.

Serve with the stuffing and Beet-Ginger Chutney (page 47).

6 TO 8 SERVINGS

STUFFING

¼ cup olive oil, divided
2 tablespoons lightly crushed almonds
½ loaf white bread, cut into 1-inch cubes (about 4 cups)
2 medium parsnips, peeled and cut into 1-inch cubes
2 cinnamon sticks
3 garlic cloves, cut in half
3 shallots, cut into ¼-inch dice
2 quinces, peeled, cored, and cut into 1-inch cubes
1 tablespoon Harissa (page 30)
1 cup chicken stock
½ cup orange juice
1 tablespoon honey
2 teaspoons chopped thyme
1 teaspoon salt
½ cup raisins
1 tablespoon chopped parsley

Heat 2 tablespoons of the olive oil in a large sauté pan over medium heat. Add the almonds and bread cubes and sauté for 5 minutes, or until golden brown. Remove from the heat and set aside.

Heat the remaining 2 tablespoons olive oil in a Dutch oven or other large pot. Add the parsnips and cinnamon sticks and sauté for about 5 minutes. Add the garlic, shallots, quinces, and harissa and sauté until the garlic is golden, about 5 minutes. Stir in the chicken stock, orange juice, and honey, reduce the heat to low, and simmer for 15 minutes.

Add the thyme, salt, raisins, and almonds and bread cubes and stir until well combined. Cook over low heat, stirring frequently, until heated through. Stir in the chopped parsley.

JERK CHICKEN

I have friends from all over the world and when we get together we often have a potluck meal, with everyone bringing a favorite dish from home. My Jamaican friend Donnovan always brings a mean jerk chicken, which is so spicy sometimes you can't eat more than a bite. I toned down the heat in this version, but it still has a really great well-balanced spicing that is characteristic of jerk dishes.

One 3- to 4-pound chicken
½ cup Jerk Mix (page 31)
2 thyme sprigs, cut in half
½ head garlic, top third cut off and papery skin removed
2 Yukon Gold potatoes, peeled and cut into 1-inch cubes
1 sweet potato, peeled and cut into 1-inch cubes
1 medium parsnip, peeled and cut into 1-inch cubes
½ medium Spanish onion, cut into 1-inch cubes
1 pear, peeled, cored, and cut into 1-inch cubes
1 quince, peeled, cored, and cut into 1-inch cubes

Preheat the oven to 350°F. Using your hand, gently loosen the skin of the chicken breast. Generously rub half of the jerk mix under and all over the breast skin. Stuff half the thyme under the skin. Put the garlic in the cavity of the chicken. Truss the chicken (see page 242). Set aside on a plate.

Combine the Yukon Gold potatoes, sweet potato, and parsnip in a large pot and add enough salted water to cover. Bring to a boil over high heat and boil for about 10 minutes, until just slightly tender. Drain.

Toss the potatoes, sweet potato, parsnip, and onion with the remaining jerk mix, then spread the vegetables in a single layer in a roasting pan. Add the remaining thyme. Place the chicken on a roasting rack above the vegetables, and roast for 45 minutes.

Add the pear and quince to the roasting pan, increase the oven temperature to 375°F, and roast for an additional 30 to 40 minutes, until an instant-read thermometer inserted in the thigh registers 160°F and the juices run clear.

Serve with Yogurt Dip (page 73).

8 SERVINGS

LEMON-OLIVE CHICKEN

One of my most vivid culinary memories is from the start of my cooking career, when I was a cook on a luxury cruise ship that traveled all over the world, stopping at local ports of call to buy fresh ingredients for that night's dinner. The market at Marrakech was my introduction to northern Africa, and to me, this dazzling market with its colorful, abundant displays of food, spices, clothing, and virtually anything else you can imagine is symbolic of Morocco and the rest of the region. Centuries ago, Marrakech became the trading mecca for spices, where European, African, and Middle Eastern merchants met to barter and exchange their wares. This ancient crossroads is still the scene of an exciting mix of cultures, with a highly specialized cuisine that reflects the region's magical past. The bright flavors of lemons, briny olives, and delicate spices are the tastes I associate with Morocco. Combining sour and salty with a balance of spices, this simple roast chicken brings me back to that long-ago day in the market of Marrakech.

One 4- to 5-pound chicken
Salt
10 green olives
5 black olives
4 garlic cloves, peeled
1 tablespoon grated lemon zest
2 shallots, roughly chopped
One 3-inch piece ginger, peeled and cut into three 1-inch pieces
2 tablespoons olive oil
Juice of 2 lemons
1 tablespoon Ras al-Hanout (page 32)

Preheat the oven to 400°F. Generously rub the body and neck cavities of the chicken with salt and sprinkle the skin with salt. Mix together the olives, garlic, lemon zest, shallots, and ginger and stuff into the body and neck cavities. Combine the olive oil, lemon juice, and Ras al-Hanout in a small bowl, and rub all over the breast and legs. Truss the chicken (see page 242).

Place the chicken on a rack in a roasting pan. Roast until an instant-read thermometer inserted in the thickest part of the thigh registers 160°F, about 60 to 70 minutes.

Transfer the chicken to a platter and let rest for 10 to 15 minutes before carving. Serve with Red Rice (page 101).

4 SERVINGS

MOROCCAN-STYLE DUCK BREASTS

When I grew up in Sweden, saffron was a spice we used during the Christmas holidays, particularly in the sweet breads we baked to celebrate the feast of St. Lucia. But this lovely, floral spice is used all along the northern and southern coasts of the Mediterranean, too, often in savory dishes. I especially like saffron as a complement to the rich and gamey meat of duck, particularly when it's paired with typical Moroccan spices. I suggest using a hen, which isn't as flavorful as the male drake but is much more tender. Scoring the breasts results in better absorption of the marinade and easier rendering of the excess fat during cooking. Leaving the duck uncovered in the refrigerator will result in a crisper skin, so plan ahead for best results.

3 cups orange juice
2 teaspoons Ras al-Hanout (page 32)
2 cloves
1 cinnamon stick
4 saffron threads
4 white cardamom pods
2 parsley sprigs, chopped
2 garlic cloves, minced, divided
2 medium red onions, diced, divided
One 3-inch piece ginger, peeled and minced, divided
Four 8-ounce boneless duck breasts
Salt
½ cup roughly chopped unsalted cashews

Bring the orange juice to a boil in a medium saucepan. Add the ras al-hanout, cloves, cinnamon stick, saffron, and cardamom and boil for 3 minutes. Add the parsley, half the garlic, half the onions, and half the ginger. Remove from the heat and let cool.

Score the skin of the duck breasts in a diamond pattern. Transfer the duck to a deep tray or baking dish. Pour the orange juice mixture over the breasts and refrigerate, uncovered, for about 2 hours.

Remove the duck breasts from the marinade and pat dry with a paper towel; reserve the marinade. Season the duck with salt. Heat a sauté pan large enough to accommodate the breasts without crowding over high heat. Add the breasts, skin side down, and cook until the skin is crisp and deeply browned, about 6 minutes. Reduce the heat to medium, turn the breasts, and cook until lightly browned and medium-rare, about 4 minutes; if you prefer duck cooked to medium, cook for 6 minutes. Transfer to a platter, reserving the fat in the pan, and let rest for 5 minutes.

While the duck breasts are resting, discard all but 2 tablespoons of fat from the pan, and heat the fat over medium heat. Add the remaining garlic, onions, and ginger, and the cashews and sauté, stirring frequently, until the onions are softened, about 4 minutes. Strain the reserved marinade into the pan, turn the heat to high, and simmer until the sauce reduces and thickens, about 5 minutes. Season with salt.

Slice the duck breasts on the diagonal, and serve with the sauce on the side and Corn Mashed Potatoes (page 94).

4 SERVINGS

JOLLOF RICE

Jollof Rice—a West African–style pilaf—is one of the best-known African dishes outside of Africa. I had it for the first time at Café Loutcha, a neighborhood restaurant in the center of Dakar. One of the national dishes of Senegal, it is served at all festive occasions, from traditional naming ceremonies to weddings and funerals. Although the recipe can vary from family to family and can highlight any combination of meat, chicken, fish, or shellfish and a variety of vegetables and spices, it is always made with enough tomatoes and palm oil to turn the rice red. In this recipe, I substitute flavorful spiced butter for the palm oil, which can be overpoweringly oily to American palates. Senegal is a Muslim country where pork is prohibited, so I use chicken sausage or turkey bacon for authenticity. You can also substitute merguez, the small, spicy sausage used throughout Muslim Africa.

¼ cup Spiced Butter (page 34) **or 4 tablespoons (½ stick) unsalted butter**

2 small chicken sausages, crumbled, or 6 slices turkey bacon, finely diced

One 3½- to 4-pound chicken, cut into 10 pieces (see page 242)

6 garlic cloves, minced

1 teaspoon chili powder

½ teaspoon ground cumin

½ teaspoon ground coriander

2 cinnamon sticks

2 teaspoons red shrimp powder (see page 101; optional)

2 medium red onions, diced

10 tomatoes, chopped, or one 28-ounce can tomatoes, drained and chopped

3 jalapeño chilies, seeds and ribs removed, finely chopped

Salt

1½ cup long-grain rice, such as basmati

3 cups chicken stock

4 scallions, trimmed and thinly sliced

2 eggs, lightly whisked

1½ cup frozen peas, thawed

Melt the butter in a Dutch oven or other large heavy pot over medium heat. When the foam subsides, add the sausage, chicken legs, thighs, and wings, the garlic, chili powder, cumin, coriander, cinnamon sticks, and red shrimp powder, if using, and sauté for 8 to 10 minutes, turning the chicken pieces once or twice, until the skin is deeply browned. If necessary, remove some of the pieces of chicken to make room to brown the breasts. Add the breasts skin side down and cook until browned, then turn and cook briefly on the second side. Transfer the breasts to a plate, and return any chicken pieces you may have removed.

Add the onions, tomatoes, jalapeños, and salt to taste and cook until the onions are softened and the oil separates from the vegetables, 15 to 20 minutes. Stir in the rice and chicken stock and return the chicken breasts to the pot. Cover the pot with a tight-fitting lid and simmer for 20 minutes, until all the liquid is absorbed and the chicken is cooked. Remove the pot from the heat and let sit, covered, for 15 minutes.

Remove the cinnamon sticks and stir in the scallions, eggs, and peas. Place the pot over medium-low heat for 2 to 3 minutes, stirring, to cook the eggs and heat the peas through. Season with salt.

6 TO 8 SERVINGS

SUN RIPENED TOMATOES
SUN RIPENED TOMATOES
SUN RIPENED TOMATOES
SUN RIPENED TOMATOES
SUN RIPENED TOMATOES
SUN RIPENED TOMATOES

Barbecued Pork Ribs

Barbecued Oxtail

Barbecued Roast Beef with Plum Sauce

Berbere-Crusted Rack of Lamb

Khayelitsha, South Africa

Boerewors Sausage Patties

Boharat Beef Skewers

Kofta Meatballs with Okra Tomato Sauce

Bobotie

MEAT

Lamb Curry

Lamb Stir-Fry

Lamb-Stuffed Tomatoes

Tea-Roasted Veal

Merguez Sausage

Roasted Veal Shanks with Apricots and Almonds

Steak Tartare

Za'atar-Roasted Leg of Lamb

Duqqa-Cured Venison Loin

W HEN YOU'RE DEALING WITH A PLACE AS DIVERSE AS THE AFRICAN CONTINENT, it's rare to come up with generalities that can be applied to the cuisine. But as people from all over Africa told me about the foods of their homeland, whether it was Morocco, Ethiopia, Kenya, Mali, or South Africa, one thing became clear: meat means celebration in Africa.

In all these places, when one of life's milestones—births, naming ceremonies, weddings, funerals—come along, the day-to-day fare of stews stretched with vegetables, starches, and breads that is designed more for filling the belly than satisfying the palate is replaced with a variety of rich and satisfying meat dishes. These celebrations aren't small gatherings—hundreds of people get together to celebrate—and they are marked with signature dishes that vary from region to region and country to country. Rarely, however, do you see the cuts of meat like beef tenderloin or rack of lamb like we have in North America. In addition, because there are so many different religions throughout the continent with so many fast days, these occasions when meat is permitted make it an even bigger deal. In the Maghreb, a lamb is roasted, while in Kenya, nyama choma—the national dish, made of grilled goat meat—is served. South Africa, the only African country I know of with a steak culture similar to that of the United States and Europe, grills fine cuts of meat along with sosaties (mutton skewers) and sausages, as well as a variety of game meats like ostrich, springbok (a kind of antelope), and giraffe. Perhaps the most unexpected meat preparation was one I saw at a wedding in Ethiopia, where kitfo, raw beef tossed with spices, was served to the five hundred guests invited to celebrate a marriage.

But meat is not just for celebrating. It's also a way of showing gratitude or respect, in a way that can be disconcerting to people who are used to their meat appearing in tidy, plastic-wrapped packages at the grocery store. A friend recounted the shock she received when the relatives she was visiting in Uganda slaughtered their finest cow in her honor. The fact that she was a vegetarian was, naturally, blithely ignored. Likewise, a live goat, ram, or cow is a common gift given to show respect or thanks to a gracious host, as owning animals is seen as a mark of wealth. A case in point is the Masai herdsmen of East Africa, who maintain huge herds of cattle but rarely slaughter them for their meat. Rather, they rely on the cow's blood and milk for sustenance. The recipes in this book are certainly not that authentic, but when you think of traditional European-style blood sausages, this Masai practice is not as bizarre as it sounds.

In this chapter, you'll find recipes that give an overview of Africa's most celebratory dishes that you find at homes or at restaurants or weddings, along with updated versions that cross my favorite African flavors with the tastes that I love. And you don't have to wait for a birth or a wedding to make them—try one of these recipes anytime you want to make an ordinary day special.

BARBECUED PORK RIBS

The West African tradition of cooking outdoors over stones was carried to the American South, forming the basis of the most beloved of Southern traditions: barbecue. I love the passion that Southern barbecue inspires—each region thinks their version is the best, whether it's the simple vinegar sauce of the Carolinas, the sweet tomato sauce of Tennessee, or the liquid fire of Texas-style barbecue. Unquestionably, my favorite meat for barbecue is pork ribs, which melt in your mouth when barbecued just right. If possible, use a charcoal grill, which will give you the smoky flavor of authentic barbecue.

2 tablespoons Berbere (page 12) or chili powder
½ teaspoon ground ginger
1 teaspoon ground cumin
½ cup packed brown sugar
¼ cup salt
3 racks baby back pork ribs (about 4 pounds)
2 tablespoons olive oil
1 medium red onion, finely chopped
2 garlic cloves, chopped
One 2-inch piece ginger, peeled and chopped
3 tomatoes, quartered, or 1½ cups chopped canned tomatoes
1 small carrot, peeled and chopped
2 tablespoons honey
½ cup water
2 tablespoons red wine vinegar
1½ teaspoons Worcestershire sauce
1 serrano chili, seeds and ribs removed, finely chopped

Combine the berbere, ground ginger, cumin, brown sugar, and salt in a small bowl. Place the ribs in a large baking pan or on a baking sheet and generously rub the berbere mixture over them. Cover and refrigerate for at least 8 hours, or overnight.

Preheat the oven to 325°F. Heat the olive oil in a large, flameproof roasting pan over medium heat. Add the onion, garlic, chopped ginger, tomatoes, and carrot and sauté until the onion is tender, about 10 minutes. Stir in the honey, water, vinegar, Worcestershire sauce, and chili.

Remove from the heat and add the ribs. Cover the pan with a lid or foil and transfer to the oven. Cook for about 2½ hours, turning the ribs every 30 minutes, until the meat has shrunk away from the ends of the rib bones and easily pulls away from the bones. Transfer the ribs to a platter, and set the roasting pan aside.

Meanwhile, prepare a medium-hot grill fire. Grill the ribs on both sides until browned but not charred, 4 to 6 minutes per side. Place on a serving platter.

Skim as much as fat as possible from the sauce, and transfer to a serving bowl. Serve the ribs with the sauce, Black-Eyed Peas (page 173), and Corn Bread (page 140).

4 TO 6 SERVINGS

BERBERE-CRUSTED RACK OF LAMB

I came up with this recipe for a dinner I was making at the Sheraton Addis Ababa in 1999, during my first visit to Ethiopia. The berbere is incredibly distinctive, giving the tender lamb an assertive, brash flavor. It's one of my first dishes to incorporate Ethiopian ingredients and flavors, and it reflects my personal philosophy as a chef: take classic flavors and add a dash of something unexpected—in this case, the potent spice blend with traditional rack of lamb.

½ cup olive oil
1½ tablespoons coarsely chopped rosemary
1 large garlic clove, smashed
2 frenched racks of lamb (1½ pounds each)
3 tablespoons Berbere (page 12), **divided**
2 teaspoons Dijon mustard
2 teaspoons beaten egg yolk
¼ cup fine bread crumbs
2 to 3 tablespoons dry red wine, divided
½ cup chicken stock
2 tablespoons cold unsalted butter, cut into pieces

Combine the oil, rosemary, and garlic in a large zipper-lock bag. Add the lamb, then seal the bag, forcing out the excess air. Marinate in the refrigerator for 8 to 24 hours, turning the bag several times.

Preheat the oven to 400°F. Make the berbere paste: Stir together 1 tablespoon of the berbere, the mustard, yolk, and bread crumbs in a small bowl, then add 1 to 2 tablespoons of the wine, just enough to make a paste. Refrigerate until ready to use.

Remove the lamb from the marinade and pat dry; discard the marinade. Heat a dry, large, heavy sauté pan over high heat until very hot. Reduce the heat to medium-high and brown the lamb, one rack at a time, about 3 minutes per side. Transfer, fat side up, to a large roasting pan.

Smear the berbere paste on the fat side of the lamb. Roast until an instant-read thermometer inserted into the center of the rack reads 125°F, for medium-rare, about 18 to 20 minutes. Transfer the lamb to a cutting board and let rest for 10 minutes.

While the lamb is roasting, toast the remaining two tablespoons berbere in a small heavy saucepan over low heat, stirring constantly, until very fragrant, about 1 minute. Add the chicken stock and 1 tablespoon wine and bring to a boil, then boil until reduced to the consistency of a sauce. Remove from the heat and whisk in the butter bit by bit until incorporated.

Cut the lamb into chops and serve the sauce on the side. Serve with Chunky Mashed Vegetables (page 176) and Awase (page 14).

6 TO 8 SERVINGS

A band of children gathered, excited by the novelty of having someone new in town.

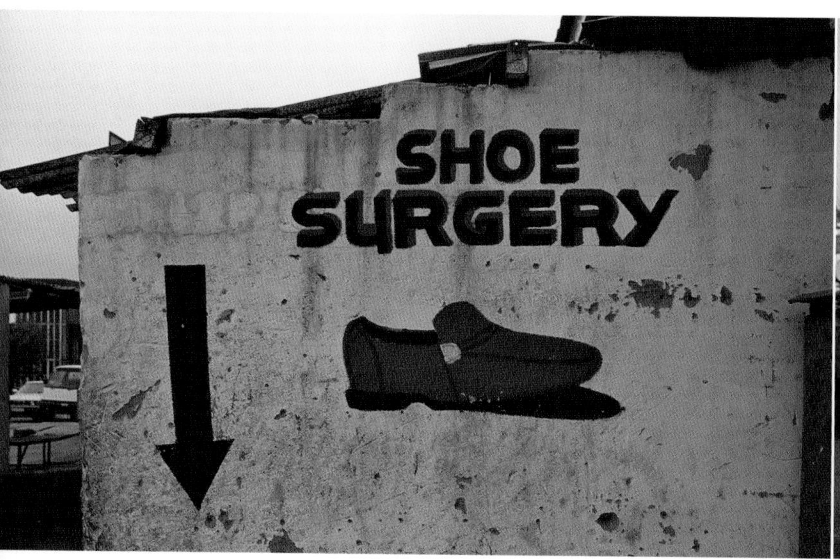

I VISITED KHAYELITSHA, A BLACK TOWNSHIP on the outskirts of Cape Town, on Freedom Day 2004. As South Africans marked ten years of democratic government, my friends and I joined in the celebration at Vicky's B&B, a four-room shack made of corrugated iron, tree trunks, and wood that is one of the best-known hotels in South Africa. It is run by Vicky Ntozini, an industrious woman with a cheerful smile who gives her guests a taste of township life. As we sat in her living room listening to stories of life in Khayelitsha, Vicky explained the significance of the colors of the South African flag, representing one nation made up of many colors: red, symbolizing the blood of the apartheid years, white for the European settlers, gold for the mineral wealth of South Africa's mines, green for the country's prosperous farming, blue for the two oceans that border the coasts, and black for the black and colored communities that dominate the country's population. She then suggested we experience Khayelitsha ourselves with a visit to the local barbecue joint, and her husband, Piksteel, offered to show us the way. Before setting off, we stopped at the local shebeen (saloon) to pick up a loaf of bread and drinks, because, as Vicky explained, at the market we would find only one thing on the menu: grilled meat.

The main road in Khayelitsha is Amandla Street, named for Nelson Mandela's rallying cry during the anti-apartheid movement. "Amandla" means "power" in the Xhosa language, and even though the dirt road was lined with rows of shacks cobbled together from pieces of corrugated steel and powered with electricity pirated from the overhead electric lines, Amandla Street filled me with hope, because the people I met there were so optimistic and supportive of the way their country is going. In just ten short years, the country has transformed itself from one of the most unjust places on earth into a functioning democracy where everyone has a voice.

As we walked through the streets, passing barbers, beauty salons, and all the other little shops that make up a town's life, a band of children gathered, excited by the novelty of having someone new in town. We formed a sort of parade moving down the dusty road. Along the way, we met the residents of Khayelitsha, many of whom had moved to the townships from the rural areas over the past decade to find work. I think it was this direct tie to rural places that gave these people such balance—although South Africa's big cities are just as modern and developed as, say, New York, if you go a little distance out you are in a completely remote place. While most people I know in the United States and Europe get their peace and balance by going to a spa, or a museum, or the movies, the people I met in Khayelitsha found theirs just by stepping outside.

As we rounded the corner near the market, we passed a man standing behind a table stacked with cow heads. Called smileys because of the way the cow's lips curl over the teeth, cow heads are a special-occasion dish in the townships, where no scrap of meat is wasted. The market itself was run by two women: one who stood behind the counter, selling the meat and brushing away flies, and the other who grilled the meat for you. I chose my piece of meat at the counter, then carried it over to the grill, where it was cooked until thoroughly charred. Sitting on a bench at one of the tables, I feasted on the meat with Piksteel and his friends, wrapping the tough, blackened meat in slices of bread, and for a brief hour was part of the community that defines the South African townships.

BOEREWORS SAUSAGE PATTIES

Mouthwateringly spicy boerewors (the word means "farmer's sausages" in Afrikaans) are one of the quintessential South African foods. I've played with the traditional recipe, making sausage patties that are easier to prepare than stuffed sausages. Freeze the bacon for 10 minutes before cutting it, as it can be difficult to chop at room temperature.

10 slices bacon, cut into ¼-inch-wide pieces
2 tablespoons Green Masala (page 27) **or curry powder**
2 tablespoons salt
3 tablespoons red wine vinegar
2 tablespoons brandy
1 tablespoon chopped chives
1 pound ground beef
1 pound ground lamb
1 pound ground veal
Barbecue Sauce (page 44)

Heat a large sauté pan over low heat. Add the bacon and cook until browned but not crisp, about 8 minutes. Add the masala and salt and cook, stirring, until very fragrant, about 5 minutes. Transfer the bacon and all the drippings to a large bowl and let cool. Add the red wine vinegar, brandy, chives, beef, lamb, and veal and mix well with your hands. Cover and refrigerate for 1 hour to blend the flavors.

Heat a grill over high heat.

Using wet hands, to prevent sticking, divide the mixture into eighths and shape into 4-inch patties.

Place the patties on the grill and cook, turning once, until deeply browned and crisped on both sides, about 4 to 5 minutes per side. Glaze the tops with a couple of spoonfuls of the barbecue sauce and flip the patties again. Glaze the second side, and continue to cook, flipping and glazing once or twice more, until the patties are coated in a caramelized layer of barbecue sauce.

Serve with grilled bread, Tarragon Mustard (page 67), and Cucumber Sambal (page 65).

8 SERVINGS

BOHARAT BEEF SKEWERS

My friend Clare comes from the Ankole kingdom in southern Uganda, where the people are known for their herds of exquisite big-horned cattle. There, beef is the meat of choice, in some cases to the exclusion of anything else: her grandmother, she told me, would only eat beef, and if a piece of fish so much as touched one of the pans in her kitchen, she would throw the pan away.

If you are a city dweller like me and don't have a grill, you can make these beef skewers by arranging the skewers in a single layer on a baking sheet and roasting for 20 minutes in a 425°F oven.

2 cups peanut oil
Juice of 4 lemons
1½ tablespoons Boharat (page 17)
4 sprigs rosemary, leaves only, finely chopped
Six 6-ounce rib-eye steaks, cut into 2-inch cubes
2 green bell peppers, cored, seeds and ribs removed, and cut into 2-inch squares
2 red bell peppers, cored, seeds and ribs removed, and cut into 2-inch squares
4 medium Spanish onions, cut into quarters
4 tomatoes, cut into 6 wedges each
6 scallions, trimmed and cut into 2-inch pieces
1 head Thyme-Roasted Garlic (page 68)

Whisk together the oil, lemon juice, boharat, and rosemary in a small bowl. Combine the beef, peppers, onions, tomatoes, and scallions in a large zipper-lock bag. Add half the boharat mixture and seal the bag, forcing out the excess air. Marinate in the refrigerator for 2 hours, turning the bag several times. Set the remaining marinade aside.

Prepare a hot grill fire. If using wooden skewers, soak in water for 30 minutes.

Squeeze the roasted garlic cloves into the reserved marinade and mix well. Set aside.

Drain the meat and vegetables, and thread onto metal or wooden skewers, alternating the meat and vegetables. Grill for 5 minutes on each side, brushing frequently with the reserved marinade. Transfer to a platter and let rest for 5 minutes.

Serve with Awase (page 14) and Warm Cabbage (page 197).

6 SERVINGS

LAMB CURRY

An understanding of spices and how to balance them seems to be built into the African palate. In almost every country, spices are used liberally, and there is a deep understanding and love for them. This may be why Indian curries are so prevalent across the continent—you find them all along the eastern coast and in South Africa's Cape Malay cuisine, which is rooted in Indian- and Indonesian-style cooking. Malay-style curries tend to be sweet and not too spicy, with a nicely balanced mix of flavors made by assembling and infusing the individual spices that make up curry powder. I've always found curry to be an easy flavor to like, particularly as a complement to the gamey taste of lamb. You could serve this with white rice, but I like the additional flavor the yellow rice brings to this dish.

½ cup Spiced Butter (page 34) **or 8 tablespoons (1 stick) unsalted butter**
2 medium red onions, sliced
Two 3-inch pieces ginger, peeled and grated
6 garlic cloves, crushed
2 bird's-eye chilies, seeds and ribs removed, finely chopped
2 teaspoons paprika
2 teaspoons ground coriander
4 cardamom pods
2 bay leaves
2 cinnamon sticks
¼ teaspoon powdered saffron
1 teaspoon ground turmeric
1 teaspoon black peppercorns
2 pounds boneless leg of lamb, cut into 2-inch cubes
6 tomatoes, chopped, or 3 cups chopped canned tomatoes
1 cup coconut milk
4 cups water
3 large Yukon Gold potatoes (1½ pounds total), peeled and cut in half
2 cups 2-inch pieces okra
1 cup plain yogurt

Melt the spiced butter in a large sauté pan over medium heat. Stir in the onions, ginger, garlic, and chilies and sauté until the onions are translucent, about 10 minutes. Add the paprika, coriander, cardamom, bay leaves, cinnamon sticks, saffron, turmeric, and peppercorns and cook, stirring constantly, until fragrant, about 30 seconds. Add the lamb and tomatoes, bring to a simmer, and simmer, uncovered, for 5 minutes. Stir in the coconut milk and 2 cups of the water and bring to a simmer, then reduce the heat to low and simmer gently for 1½ hours.

Add the remaining 2 cups water and simmer, uncovered, for 40 minutes. Add the potatoes, cover, and simmer until the meat is tender, about 40 minutes longer.

Add the okra and cook for 10 minutes, or until tender. Remove from the heat, remove the bay leaves, and stir in the yogurt.

Serve with Yellow Rice (page 105).

6 TO 8 SERVINGS

LAMB STIR-FRY

Stir-fry is thought of as an Asian-style food, but Africa has its stir-fries too, particularly sukuma wiki, one of the national dishes of Kenya. There, the focus would be on the greens—usually collard greens, with a little bit of beef or goat meat for flavor—but I've adapted it to showcase lamb and kale. To get the beautifully seared meat of a perfect stir-fry, you need intensely high heat and a pan with a big surface area so that the heat can penetrate the meat quickly. A wok or cast-iron skillet can help you get the high heat you need, but if you don't have one you can make do with a large heavy skillet.

2 tablespoons peanut oil
1 medium red onion, sliced
½ teaspoon ground cardamom, preferably freshly ground
½ teaspoon ground cumin
2 garlic cloves, minced
One 2-inch piece ginger, peeled and grated
8 ounces kale, cleaned and shredded
1½ pounds boneless lamb loin, cut into ½-inch-thick slices
½ teaspoon salt
4 tomatoes, chopped, or 2 cups chopped canned tomatoes
Freshly ground black pepper

Heat the oil in a wok or large heavy skillet over high heat. Add the onion, cardamom, cumin, garlic, and ginger and sauté until the onion is translucent, about 3 minutes. Add the kale and sauté until wilted, about 4 minutes. Remove from the pan with tongs and set aside.

Add the lamb to the hot pan and stir-fry until browned on all sides. Sprinkle with the salt, add the tomatoes, and simmer for 5 minutes.

Return the kale mixture to the pan and stir until heated through, 3 to 5 minutes. Season with pepper and remove from the heat.

Serve with Chunky Mashed Vegetables (page 176).

4 TO 6 SERVINGS

LAMB STIR-FRY

Stir-fry is thought of as an Asian-style food, but Africa has its stir-fries too, particularly sukuma wiki, one of the national dishes of Kenya. There, the focus would be on the greens—usually collard greens, with a little bit of beef or goat meat for flavor—but I've adapted it to showcase lamb and kale. To get the beautifully seared meat of a perfect stir-fry, you need intensely high heat and a pan with a big surface area so that the heat can penetrate the meat quickly. A wok or cast-iron skillet can help you get the high heat you need, but if you don't have one you can make do with a large heavy skillet.

2 tablespoons peanut oil
1 medium red onion, sliced
½ teaspoon ground cardamom, preferably freshly ground
½ teaspoon ground cumin
2 garlic cloves, minced
One 2-inch piece ginger, peeled and grated
8 ounces kale, cleaned and shredded
1½ pounds boneless lamb loin, cut into ½-inch-thick slices
½ teaspoon salt
4 tomatoes, chopped, or 2 cups chopped canned tomatoes
Freshly ground black pepper

Heat the oil in a wok or large heavy skillet over high heat. Add the onion, cardamom, cumin, garlic, and ginger and sauté until the onion is translucent, about 3 minutes. Add the kale and sauté until wilted, about 4 minutes. Remove from the pan with tongs and set aside.

Add the lamb to the hot pan and stir-fry until browned on all sides. Sprinkle with the salt, add the tomatoes, and simmer for 5 minutes.

Return the kale mixture to the pan and stir until heated through, 3 to 5 minutes. Season with pepper and remove from the heat.

Serve with Chunky Mashed Vegetables (page 176).

4 TO 6 SERVINGS

LAMB-STUFFED TOMATOES

This North African–inspired dish is one of my favorites for entertaining because you can prepare the tomatoes and the stuffing in advance, then quickly cook and assemble them while your guests are enjoying cocktails. For a more elaborate preparation, slow-roast the tomatoes in a 300°F oven for 40 minutes before stuffing them, which will intensify their flavor.

2 pounds ground lamb
2 teaspoons Boharat (page 17)
6 large tomatoes
2 tablespoons olive oil, plus extra for drizzling
2 medium red onions, roughly chopped
1 teaspoon salt
¾ cup long-grain rice
4 garlic cloves, minced
2 Scotch bonnet chilies, seeds and ribs removed, finely chopped
1 eggplant, cut into 1-inch cubes
3 cups chicken stock
2 dill sprigs, chopped

Combine the ground lamb and boharat in a medium bowl and mix well with your hands. Cover and refrigerate for 20 minutes.

Preheat the oven to 350°F. Slice the tops from the tomatoes. Spoon out the pulp and seeds and reserve. Brush a baking sheet with olive oil. Arrange the tomatoes on the baking sheet and bake for 10 minutes. Set aside on the baking sheet.

Heat the 2 tablespoons olive oil in a large pot over high heat. Add the onions, the spiced lamb, and salt and sauté for about 10 minutes, until the meat is browned. Add the rice, garlic, chilies, eggplant, and the reserved tomato pulp and cook, stirring frequently, for 5 minutes. Add the chicken stock, bring to a simmer, and simmer, uncovered, for 20 minutes, until the rice is tender. Remove from the heat.

Preheat the oven to 350°F. Divide the lamb stuffing evenly among the tomatoes and bake for 10 minutes, to heat through and blend the flavors.

Drizzle the tomatoes with olive oil and sprinkle with dill. Serve hot or at room temperature, with Lentil Stew (page 123).

6 SERVINGS

TEA-ROASTED VEAL

Cooking with tea gives meats an earthy flavor. I have long been a fan of using tea when cooking, and when I first tried rooibos, the herbal red bush tea that is a favorite in South Africa, I immediately thought this delicately fragrant liquid would be excellent for curing meats. Rooibos is starting to become available in the United States, but if you can't find red tea at your local market, substitute black tea.

¼ cup salt
2 cups water
½ cup red wine vinegar
1 rosemary sprig, leaves only, minced
¼ cup honey
One 3-inch piece ginger, peeled and chopped
¼ cup red tea leaves or the leaves from 3 tea bags
½ vanilla bean
One 2-pound boneless veal shoulder roast
2 tablespoons Chermoula (page 15)

Combine the salt, water, and vinegar in a saucepan and bring to a boil. Add the rosemary, honey, ginger, and tea leaves. With a sharp paring knife, cut the vanilla bean lengthwise in half, and use the back of the knife to scrape the seeds into the pan. Add the vanilla bean. Bring back to a boil, then reduce the heat and simmer for 5 minutes. Remove from the heat and let cool.

Place the veal in a baking dish. Reserve ½ cup of the tea mixture, and pour the rest over the veal. Cover and refrigerate for at least 8 hours, or overnight, turning occasionally.

Preheat the oven to 325°F. Remove the veal from the tea mixture and pat dry. Smear the roast with the chermoula, and place the veal on a rack in a roasting pan.

Roast the veal for 1 to 1½ hours, basting often with the reserved tea marinade, until an instant-read thermometer inserted into the thickest part of the roast registers 130°F. Tent with foil and let rest for 20 minutes before serving.

Serve with Warm Eggplant-Butternut Squash Salad (page 86).

4 SERVINGS

MERGUEZ SAUSAGE

Although you can find merguez sausages in Europe and the United States, I associate them with Ramadan because many of the Muslim staff members at Aquavit bring it in to break their fast during the monthlong religious celebration. Unlike many other sausages, which are made with pork, merguez sausages originated in North Africa, where they are made with lamb or beef to comply with Islamic law and spiced with fiery harissa, which gives them heat and a beautiful red color. In this version, I've simplified the process by making merguez without the traditional sausage casing.

1 teaspoon ground cumin
1 teaspoon ground coriander
1 teaspoon cayenne pepper
2 pounds ground lamb
8 ounces ground dark chicken meat
4 garlic cloves, minced
2 teaspoons Harissa (page 30)
2 teaspoons salt
1½ tablespoons chopped parsley
1 tablespoon chopped mint
½ cup olive oil

Toast the cumin, coriander, and cayenne in a small sauté pan until aromatic, about 30 seconds. Remove from the heat and let cool.

Combine the toasted spices, lamb, chicken, garlic, harissa, salt, parsley, and mint in a large bowl and mix well with your hands. Cover and refrigerate for 1 hour to allow the flavors to blend.

Preheat the oven to 350°F. Using wet hands, to keep the mixture from sticking, shape the lamb mixture into golf-ball-sized balls. You should have about 24 balls.

Heat the oil in a large skillet over medium-high heat. Add the meatballs, in batches if necessary, and brown on all sides, turning frequently, about 8 minutes. Remove from the pan and drain on paper towels.

Arrange the meatballs on a baking sheet and bake for 10 minutes, or until cooked through.

Serve with Tomato Sauce (page 71) and Warm Potato-Cod Salad (page 87).

4 TO 6 SERVINGS

ROASTED VEAL SHANKS WITH APRICOTS AND ALMONDS

The floral, fragrant flavors of apricots and almonds complement roasted veal in this special-occasion dish from Morocco that's served at weddings and to honored guests. In the traditional version, dried apricots are soaked overnight before being added to the sauce. This version, using fresh and dried apricots, is less time-consuming but just as special. Whole veal shanks, even if you can find them, are very large and probably too big for most home cooks' pots. Your butcher or grocer will probably stock veal shanks in large slices, which is ideal for this recipe.

8 slices veal shank, ½ inch thick
3 cups Yogurt Rub (page 35)
3 tablespoons olive oil
2 medium Spanish onions, sliced
2 cups dry white wine
6 ripe apricots, sliced
Juice of 2 lemons
6 dried apricots, chopped
4 cloves garlic, minced
2 cups chopped blanched almonds
2 cups couscous
4 tarragon sprigs, leaves only

Preheat the oven to 250°F. Rub the veal shanks all over with the yogurt rub until well coated. Arrange the veal in a roasting pan in a single layer, cover, and roast for 2 hours.

Remove 1 cup of the cooking liquid from the roasting pan and set aside. Increase the heat to 350°F and roast until the shanks are tender, about another 30 minutes.

Meanwhile, heat the olive oil in a large pot over medium heat. Add the onions and cook, stirring frequently, until translucent, 5 to 7 minutes. Add the wine, fresh apricots, lemon juice, and the reserved cooking juices, bring to a simmer, and simmer for 30 minutes. Stir in the dried apricots, garlic, and almonds and simmer for another 15 minutes.

While the apricots are cooking, cook the couscous according to the package directions. Set aside.

Add the couscous and tarragon to the apricots and stir to heat through.

To serve, heap the couscous on a large serving platter and arrange the veal shanks around it.

8 SERVINGS

STEAK TARTARE

Legend has it that kitfo—the Ethiopian Steak Tartare that inspired this recipe—came about during one of the many wars between the Christian Gurage tribe and the Muslims, when the Gurages were hiding out in the mountains and needed to develop quick-cooking meals they could prepare without attracting attention from big, smoking fires. It's now a special-occasion dish, served at weddings and other celebratory events. Although traditionally it is served almost raw in Ethiopia, you can prepare this stir-fry-style steak to whatever degree of doneness you desire.

2 pounds beef tenderloin

½ cup Spiced Butter (page 34) **or 8 tablespoons (1 stick) unsalted butter**

1 tablespoon Berbere (page 12) **or chili powder**

2 teaspoons ground cardamom, preferably freshly ground

1 teaspoon salt

¼ teaspoon freshly ground black pepper

Grind or very finely chop the beef.

Melt the butter in a large sauté pan over low heat. Add the berbere, cardamom, salt, and pepper and stir until well combined. Add the ground beef, remove from the heat, and mix well.

Serve immediately, with Awase (page 14) and Mango Sambal (page 64).

4 SERVINGS

ZA'ATAR-ROASTED LEG OF LAMB

Where I grew up, pork roast or roast beef was the meat of choice for festive celebrations. But in other parts of the world, particularly Arabic North Africa, lamb holds the place of honor as the centerpiece of any important occasion. In this preparation, leg of lamb—a relatively inexpensive cut of meat—is transformed into an elegant showpiece by slow-roasting it with za'atar, which results in incredibly tender meat with deliciously intense flavors. It's equally good served hot from the oven or at room temperature.

¾ cup Za'atar (page 37)
½ cup Black Olive Oil (page 15)
½ cup olive oil
1½ teaspoons salt
One 7- to 8-pound bone-in leg of lamb
4 sprigs rosemary, 2 chopped, 2 left whole
2 heads garlic, papery skin removed
2 medium Spanish onions, cut into quarters
2 medium red onions, cut into quarters
1 cup dry red wine

Preheat the oven to 250°F. Whisk together the za'atar, both oils, and the salt in a small bowl. Rub over the lamb leg to thoroughly coat.

Place the 2 whole rosemary sprigs in the bottom of a roasting pan. Transfer the lamb to the pan, fat side up, and roast for 2 hours.

Scatter the garlic, chopped rosemary, Spanish onions, and red onions around the lamb and add the red wine to the pan. Increase the oven temperature to 350°F and roast for another 45 minutes, or until an instant-read thermometer inserted in the thickest part of the meat reaches 125°F.

Transfer the lamb to a cutting board and let rest for 15 minutes before carving and serving.

Serve with Citrus Cabbage Salad (page 77).

6 SERVINGS

DUQQA-CURED VENISON LOIN

With the land's abundance of wildlife, game is a common delicacy on South African tables. During my African travels, I sampled many different types of game, including springbok, an antelope with a delicately gamey flavor, which inspired this recipe. Because springbok is difficult to find in U.S. markets, I substitute venison, which is darker in color but similar in flavor and texture. Note that the cured meat is cooked only briefly and cut thinly, resulting in a carpacciolike presentation.

2½ cups Duqqa (page 19), **divided**
1 cup packed brown sugar
Grated zest of 2 lemons
1 tablespoon roughly chopped parsley
1 tablespoon roughly chopped cilantro
Two 3-inch pieces ginger, peeled and grated
4 garlic cloves, minced
One 2-pound venison loin
3 tablespoons olive oil, divided

Combine 2 cups of the duqqa, the sugar, lemon zest, parsley, cilantro, ginger, and garlic in a bowl. Place the venison loin in a deep container and rub all over with the duqqa mix. Cover and refrigerate for 12 hours, turning occasionally. (As the venison sits, the cure mix will become liquid.)

Remove the venison from the curing liquid, rinse, and pat dry. Rub the loin with 1 tablespoon of the olive oil, then rub with the remaining ½ cup duqqa.

Heat the remaining 2 tablespoons oil in a large sauté pan over high heat. Add the venison loin and sear for 30 seconds. Turn and sear on the other side for 30 seconds. Remove the venison from the pan and cut into ¼-inch-thick slices.

Serve with Beet-Ginger Chutney (page 47).

4 SERVINGS

Carlsberg

Almond Cookies

Avocado Fool

Banana Fritters

Bissap Granité

District Six, Cape Town, South Africa

Chocolate-Coconut Sorbet with Peanut Butter

Caramelized Mango Soup with Poppy Seed Rice Pudding

Chocolate Pancakes with Bananas Flambé

Chocolate Rum Cake with Cinnamon Whipped Cream

Ginger-Banana Salad with Honey Ice Cream

DESSERTS AND DRINKS

Koesisters

Malva Pudding

Mango-Papaya Kulfi

Peanut Cake with Caramelized Papayas and Plums

Pineapple-Cashew Salad

Sesame Cookies

Sour Tamarind-Almond Balls

Tangerine Consommé with Tapioca

Sweet Potato–Coconut Turnovers

Ginger Beer

Mint Iced Tea

Lemongrass Tisane

Tamarind Drink

W**HEN I WAS A YOUNG CHEF IN SWEDEN AND FRANCE,** it was drilled into my head that a meal followed a prescribed course: appetizer, entrée, dessert. But as I quickly learned when I began to travel outside of Europe, dessert in the way that I knew it is a very Western phenomenon. Wherever I went in the tropics—whether it was the Amazon, Thailand, West Africa, Ethiopia—I found one common denominator: in all the warm climates, the end of most meals is marked not with cakes or tarts or pies, but with fruit, served as simply as possible.

This similarity struck me and set me to wondering why these very different places had all evolved cuisines without a tradition of baking. I noticed a few similarities in the cultures that seem to explain the absence of dessert. First off, food isn't eaten in courses as I was accustomed to. This is classic poor man's cooking, and the point of eating is not to savor every morsel, but for a more basic reason: to fill up your belly so you can get your work done. After a hearty meal of ugali in Kenya, or pad thai in Thailand, or feijoada in Brazil, it only makes sense to have a light and refreshing ending. And perhaps just as important, these are tropical climates where the greatest fruit in the world can be found year round, so there's no need to make sweet treats—they literally grow on trees.

This realization made me rethink my idea of what dessert is. Throughout my travels, I found that meals usually end with fresh fruit like pineapple slices, orange wedges, mango chunks, or bananas sprinkled with a little sugar or honey. It's a refreshing and healthy way to end a meal, and on a hot and humid day or after a heavy meal, far preferable to a creamy rich cake or pudding. Now I find myself planning my meals the African way: if I want to make a heavy, rich dessert, I'll serve a lighter meal, like a salad and shrimp piri piri, and when I'm making a heavy main course, I'll bring the meal to a close with an orange or a few cookies.

Of course, this isn't to say that desserts are unknown in Africa. Everywhere I traveled there were pastry shops, a nice little luxury that's rooted in Europe but has taken on a life of its own in Africa. Because many people in Africa's Muslim cultures don't gather in bars or pubs to drink alcohol, these pastry shops take on the role of meeting place—the spot where people in a community can gather to discuss the day's events, plan for the future, or just kick back and relax. When there is something to celebrate—a wedding, a birthday, a funeral, a naming ceremony—each region has its own special-occasion desserts, and the women gather in the kitchen for days beforehand, baking up a smorgasbord of cakes and pastries.

I did discover two distinctly different regions with a strong dessert tradition. In South Africa, where the Dutch culinary influences remain strong, there is an incredibly diverse range of cakes and pastries that are part of the national culinary tradition. I was also fascinated by the distinctive desserts of Morocco that have a purely Arabic sensibility, with pastries doused in honey or sprinkled with orange water, not dusted with powdered sugar or drizzled with sauce, as

I was used to seeing. In some cases, "dessert" in Morocco was a part of the main course, as in the Moroccan b'steeya, a traditional pie made of layers of stewed pigeon and sweetened almonds wrapped in a thin pastry called warqa and flavored with cinnamon and sugar.

In this chapter you'll also find recipes for a few beverages that represent the tastes of the continent. South Africa is the only country I visited with a strong European-style wine tradition, but other regions have their own traditional drinks: fruit juices and punches, lemonade, tea, coffee served espresso style, and beer. Ethiopia even has tej, the home-brewed honey-based wine that is the signature drink of the country.

The recipes in this chapter are inspired by the spirit of Africa—they feature flavors that I discovered or grew to appreciate in my travels. Whether you're capping off an African feast or just want to close a meal with something new, I hope you'll find that one of these desserts brings a happy ending to your meal.

ALMOND COOKIES

Almonds play a big part in Moroccan cooking, making an appearance in both sweet and savory dishes. They are the basis for qa'b el-ghazal (horns of the doe), a crescent-shaped pastry with an almond and sugar filling that is almost always served with sweetened mint tea to visitors in Moroccan homes. This cookie is a variation of that traditional pastry that is much less time-consuming to make, but just as delicious. If you can't find almond flour, process 1 cup sliced blanched almonds into a powder in a food processor.

1¾ cups all-purpose flour
1½ cups almond flour
½ teaspoon salt
½ pound (2 sticks) unsalted butter, at room temperature
½ cup sugar
About 1½ cups blanched whole almonds

Sift the flour, almond flour, and salt into a bowl; set aside.

With an electric mixer, cream the butter and sugar in a large bowl. Add the flour mixture and beat until combined. Turn the dough out onto a lightly floured surface and knead for 1 to 2 minutes, until the dough forms a ball. Wrap in plastic and refrigerate for 15 minutes.

Preheat the oven to 325°F. Line two baking sheets with parchment paper or grease them with butter. Shape the dough into 1-inch balls and arrange on the baking sheets, leaving about 2 inches between the cookies. Press an almond into the center of each cookie, flattening it slightly.

Bake for 10 to 15 minutes, until golden. Remove from the baking sheets and cool on a wire rack.

MAKES ABOUT 5 DOZEN COOKIES

AVOCADO FOOL

English settlers introduced very few of their native dishes to their colonies on the African continent. Fool is one exception. This rich, creamy, quintessentially British dessert became a favorite and is now served throughout West Africa. Fool is typically made with berries, but here I make it with avocado, an unusual but delicious departure that takes a flavor typically used in salads and appetizers and puts it to use to bring a meal to a close in the same way a cheese course is served—its unusual, mildly vegetal flavor has a mousselike texture with just a hint of sweetness.

3 ripe avocados
¾ cup sweetened condensed milk
Juice of 1 lime
¾ cup heavy cream

Pit and peel 2 of the avocados and cut into 1-inch chunks. Combine the avocado chunks, condensed milk, and lime juice in a food processor and puree until smooth. Set aside.

Whip the cream in a large bowl until soft peaks form. Fold in the avocado puree.

Just before serving, pit and peel the remaining avocado and cut into thin slices.

To serve, spoon the fool into martini glasses and garnish with the avocado slices.

4 SERVINGS

BANANA FRITTERS

Bananas in all forms—green, yellow, plantains—are eaten throughout Africa, both as a savory side dish and for dessert. Here, bananas play the starring role in a simple, crispy fritter that makes a great dessert or sweet snack. The batter is runny, so the fritters will be varied in size and shape.

3 ripe bananas
½ cup fine cornmeal
1 teaspoon sugar
¼ teaspoon salt
3 to 4 cups canola oil for deep-frying
2 tablespoons honey

Combine the bananas, cornmeal, sugar, and salt in a bowl and mash with a fork until smooth.

Heat 2½ inches of oil in a deep pot to 350°F. Working in batches, add the banana mixture, a heaping tablespoon at a time, and fry until golden brown, about 2 to 3 minutes, turning once halfway through cooking. Remove from the oil with a skimmer or slotted spoon and drain on paper towels.

Before serving, drizzle with the honey.

MAKES 12 FRITTERS

BISSAP GRANITÉ

The first time one of my friends from Gambia came to visit, she brought bissap, a traditional sweetened tea brewed from hibiscus leaves. I loved the unusual floral taste, and ever since I've been looking for an opportunity to incorporate the taste of bissap in new ways. This icy granité is a refreshing treat, on its own or with fresh strawberries.

Dried hibiscus flowers can be challenging to find. Look for them in specialty markets, health food stores, African or West Indian markets, or tea shops. They can be overwhelmingly astringent, so take care not to oversteep the dried blossoms. If you can't find hibiscus flowers, substitute 5 cups of cranberry juice for the hibiscus liquid. The flavor won't be the same, but you'll get a similar color and texture.

If you have a metal baking pan, use that: the granité will freeze much faster in metal than in glass.

1 vanilla bean
1 cup sugar
¼ cup fresh lemon juice
4 cups water
1½ cups dried hibiscus flowers
8 mint leaves, finely shredded, for garnish

With a sharp knife, split the vanilla bean lengthwise, then use the back of the knife to scrape out the seeds. Combine the seeds, pod, sugar, lemon juice, and water in a large saucepan and bring to a boil. Remove from the heat, add the hibiscus flowers, cover, and let steep for 10 minutes.

Strain the liquid, and pour it into a shallow baking pan. Put the pan in the freezer. After 30 minutes, drag a fork back and forth through the partially frozen mixture to break it up into tiny crystals. Repeat every 30 minutes until the granité has the texture of shaved ice.

To serve, scrape out the granité into eight tall glasses with a fork, and garnish with the mint.

8 SERVINGS

We set off through the remains of District 6 in search of the real thing.

I WAS IN PAARL, A QUAINT SMALL CITY in the Cape Winelands an hour or so northeast of Cape Town, and my itinerary included a stay at a bed-and-breakfast and dinner at some of the area's finest restaurants. How I got from there to a tiny kitchen in Cape Town's District Six is one of those happy accidents that makes travel such an adventure.

One Saturday night during my stay in Paarl, I was eating dinner and sampling South African wines at Marc's Mediterranean Cuisine—a delightful restaurant owned by the gracious and charming Marc Friedrich—when I noticed a man dining by himself. Earlier in the day, I'd seen him at the inn, so I invited him to join my friends and me at our table. His name was Owen Juilles and, as luck would have it, he was the chef for South African Airlines. When I told him I was in South Africa to research a book about African food, he immediately volunteered to show us around Cape Town and introduce us to the food of his heritage: Cape Malay, the beautiful blend of Malaysian, Indian, African, and European cooking that is perhaps the most celebrated cuisine in Africa.

The Cape Malays descended from Indonesians, Sri Lankans, Indians, and Malaysians who were captured and enslaved in the seventeenth and eighteenth centuries by the Dutch East India Company and brought to Cape Town. These slaves created a hybrid cuisine, melding the curries, the chilies, and the spices such as ginger, cinnamon, and turmeric from their homelands with the dull, less flavorful cooking of their Dutch masters. I'd read about the Cape Malay magic for years, and was eager to see and taste firsthand its signature combinations of meat cooked with fruit and the marriage of sweet and savory flavors with hints of spice, curry, and other seasonings.

Owen enthusiastically recounted the Cape Malay dishes I had to try—bobotie, the spicy meat casserole; the pickled fish known as ingelegte vis; blatjang, a ketchuplike condiment served at every meal; smoorjtie, a tomato-based stew that typically accompanies the South African fish snoek; and bookem, a big, dried sardine that's eaten like jerky. But most important of all, he said, were koesisters, the traditional doughnutlike pastry served with coffee in all Cape Malay homes every Sunday morning.

The next morning, we set off for the neighborhood where Owen had grown up, District Six, the formerly vibrant Malay neighborhood that was once known as the soul of Cape Town. "Here is where we will find real koesisters," he told me. According to Owen, authentic koesisters could not be found at a bakery but must be purchased from a Cape Malay woman who made them in her home. So we set off through the remains of District Six in search of the real thing.

A girl we passed on the street pointed us to a house where koesisters were sold. Entering the front door, we descended a flight of dark stairs into a narrow house. At the back was a small kitchen, where Gadijah Carim makes and

sells doughnuts every Sunday. A petite, soft-spoken Muslim, she shyly told us that she makes a thousand koesisters every week to sell to people in the neighborhood as well as to the nearby District Six Museum, which takes six hundred pastries each week.

She was surprised by my interest in her koesisters, but nevertheless was happy to demonstrate how she cooked the spiced dough in hot oil, then boiled the pastries in simple syrup before dusting them with coconut flakes. During our visit, a stream of people came to her front door, each bringing a container that she filled with koesisters to be taken home and eaten after church.

As she made the koesisters, she was also preparing Sunday dinner, a time when Malay families gather each week. On the menu was the typical Cape Malay Sunday feast: curry, stir-fry, vegetables, roasted pumpkin, and a beet salad. These aromas filled her kitchen and proved that in this modern, world-class city, tradition and family still prevail.

During my stay in Cape Town, I tried the other Cape Malay specialties Owen urged me to sample, and of all the foods I tried in Africa, Cape Malay became my favorite. But for me, the defining experience of Cape Malay cuisine was eating those steaming hot, freshly baked koesisters, made by hand in Gadijah Carim's tiny kitchen.

CHOCOLATE-COCONUT SORBET WITH PEANUT BUTTER

I wanted to develop a new dessert that used ingredients from all over Africa and had familiar flavors that most people like. The chocolate-coconut sorbet I came up with is an example of how I like to devise desserts—I take an elegant component, like the sorbet, and combine it with a simple homey flavor, like the peanut butter, in the hopes of getting something that's new and exciting. If you don't have an ice cream maker, you can transfer the sorbet base to a metal bowl and freeze it. You won't get the same velvety texture but you'll still have the wonderfully rich, chocolaty flavor. Served with fresh fruit, this dessert serves up some of my favorite flavors.

One 14-ounce can coconut milk
2¼ cups water
1⅔ cups granulated sugar
⅓ cup packed brown sugar
1 vanilla bean
One 3-inch piece ginger, peeled and thickly sliced
2 cups unsweetened cocoa powder
Peanut Butter (recipe follows)

Combine the coconut milk, water, and both sugars in a medium saucepan and place over medium heat. With a sharp knife, split the vanilla bean lengthwise, then use the back of the knife to scrape out the seeds. Stir the seeds, pod, and ginger into the coconut milk mixture, bring to a simmer, and simmer, stirring, until the sugar dissolves, about 5 minutes. Whisk in the cocoa and bring back to a simmer. Simmer for 2 minutes, stirring constantly. Transfer to a medium bowl.

Discard the vanilla pod and ginger slices, and refrigerate the mixture for 2 hours, or until completely cold.

Pour the chilled mixture into an ice cream maker and process according to the manufacturer's instructions. The sorbet will be soft and creamy. For a firmer consistency, transfer the sorbet to an airtight container and place in freezer for at least 2 hours; remove from the freezer about 15 minutes before serving.

To serve, scoop the sorbet into bowls, and top each with a dollop of peanut butter.

8 SERVINGS

PEANUT BUTTER

2 cups roasted peanuts
½ cup sugar, or to taste
Salt
2 tablespoons peanut oil, if needed

Combine the peanuts, sugar, and a large pinch of salt in a food processor and grind to chunky paste; if the mixture seems dry, or if the processor blade isn't catching the nuts to grind them, add the peanut oil as needed. If necessary, add salt or sugar to taste.

CARAMELIZED MANGO SOUP WITH POPPY SEED RICE PUDDING

Like me, this dessert is a hybrid of Africa and the Western world—it combines the tropical flavor of mango with a rice pudding that showcases poppy seeds, a popular flavoring used in many European-style desserts. I've caramelized the mangoes to add another flavor dimension and make this dish a standout. For the best results, use the ripest, juiciest mangoes you can find.

1 tablespoon unsalted butter
2 soft ripe mangoes, peeled, pitted, and cut into 1-inch dice (about 2 cups)
½ cup sugar
One 3-inch piece ginger, peeled
2 cardamon pods
1 cinnamon stick
1 cup fresh orange juice
½ cup dry white wine
Juice of 4 limes
Poppy Seed Rice Pudding (recipe follows)

Melt the butter in a large sauté pan over medium heat. Add the mangoes, sugar, ginger, cardamom, and cinnamon stick and sauté until the mangoes begin to caramelize, about 7 minutes. Pour in the orange juice and white wine and bring to a simmer, then reduce the heat to low and simmer for 10 minutes. Remove from the heat and let cool.

Remove the ginger, cardamom pods, and cinnamon stick and transfer the mixture to a blender. Puree until smooth, then add the lime juice. Refrigerate until chilled.

Using a sharp knife, cut the rice pudding into 4-inch squares. Place one rice pudding square in each of six shallow bowls. Ladle the soup over the rice and serve immediately.

6 SERVINGS

POPPY SEED RICE PUDDING

1 tablespoon unsalted butter
2 vanilla beans
1 cinnamon stick
1 cup short-grain rice
1½ tablespoons poppy seeds
¼ cup sugar
1 lemongrass stalk, trimmed and crushed
2 cups milk
One 14-ounce can coconut milk
6 mint leaves, finely chopped
Grated zest of 2 limes

Line a 13 x 9-inch baking dish with waxed paper. Set aside.

Melt the butter in a large sauté pan over medium heat. With a sharp knife, split the vanilla beans lengthwise, then use the back of the knife to scrape out the seeds. Add the vanilla seeds, pods, cinnamon stick, rice, poppy seeds, sugar, and lemongrass to the pan and sauté for 2 minutes, or until fragrant. Pour in the milk and coconut milk, bring to a simmer, and simmer for 5 minutes. Cover, reduce the heat to low, and let simmer for 30 minutes, or until most of the liquid is absorbed and the rice is very tender. Discard the cinnamon and vanilla pod.

Stir in the mint leaves and lime zest, then spread the mixture in the prepared baking dish. Cover with plastic wrap and refrigerate until chilled.

CHOCOLATE PANCAKES WITH BANANAS FLAMBÉ

The inspiration for this dessert came from an afternoon I spent on Ile de Goree, a lively little island shaded by palm trees and purple bougainvillea just off the coast of Senegal. I ate lunch with my friends at a beachside shack, while swarms of children and young-at-heart adults played in the surf before us. Our meal ended with a plate of bananas flambé, and from then on I've always associated this classic French preparation with that idyllic day.

Here, the bananas are served with a moist and chocolaty pancake. To make the pancakes, it's best to use a really high-quality chocolate, like Valrhona, for the most intense taste. You can also use the pancake batter to make robustly flavored cupcakes or cake—just pour the batter into greased pans and bake at 350°F until a skewer inserted into the center comes out clean.

4 ounces bittersweet chocolate, coarsely chopped
8 tablespoons (1 stick) unsalted butter, cut into chunks, plus 2 to 3 tablespoons unsalted butter, at room temperature
2 large eggs
2 large egg yolks
2 tablespoons plus 2 teaspoons sugar
5 tablespoons all-purpose flour
Bananas Flambé (recipe follows)

Melt the chocolate and the 8 tablespoons butter in the top of a double boiler or in a heatproof bowl over a saucepan of barely simmering water, stirring occasionally until smooth. Remove from the heat.

Whisk together the eggs, egg yolks, and sugar in a large bowl until well mixed. Whisk in the warm melted chocolate and butter. Sift the flour over the top and fold it in.

Melt 1 tablespoon butter over low heat in a large nonstick sauté pan. Drop batter by heaping tablespoons into the pan and cook for 2 minutes, then turn and cook on the other side. Transfer the pancakes to a plate. Repeat with remaining batter, adding more butter to the pan as necessary.

Serve the pancakes on a platter with the bananas.

Note: The pancakes can be made in advance. Before serving, reheat in a 350°F oven until heated through.

6 TO 8 SERVINGS

BANANAS FLAMBÉ

½ cup roasted cashews, roughly chopped
1 cinnamon stick
½ cup honey
½ cup packed brown sugar
1 vanilla bean
2 bananas, cut lengthwise in half, then cut crosswise into slices
¼ cup dark rum
Juice of 2 limes
2 tablespoons unsalted butter, cut into pieces

Toast the cashews and cinnamon stick in a medium sauté pan over low heat for 3 to 4 minutes, until the cinnamon smells fragrant. Set aside to cool.

Combine the honey and brown sugar in a large sauté pan and cook over high heat, stirring, until the brown sugar dissolves and the mixture begins to bubble. With a sharp knife, split the vanilla bean lengthwise, then use the back of the knife to scrape out the seeds. Add the seeds, pod, bananas, and cashews and cinnamon stick and sauté for 2 to 3 minutes, until heated through. Remove from the heat, carefully pour in the rum, and return to the heat; don't lean over the pan, as the rum will flame up. If the rum doesn't flame, carefully light a match and hold it at the edge of the pan; the fumes of the warmed rum should flame up immediately. The flames will extinguish after the alcohol is burned off, about 1 minute.

Add the lime juice and remove from the heat. Swirl in the butter until melted. Remove the cinnamon stick and vanilla pod, and serve warm.

CHOCOLATE RUM CAKE WITH CINNAMON WHIPPED CREAM

In Ethiopia there is no cultural tradition of dessert, but all the pastry shops sell beautiful frosted cakes. The grandest of all of them is chocolate cake—rich, dense, and satisfying. It's always served at celebrations and is the perfect gift for a special someone. This cake was inspired by those cakes I saw in the Addis Ababa shops. It also is a tribute to the spice farm I visited in Zanzibar, where I tasted freshly harvested "true" cinnamon—also known as canela—for the first time. More complex and fragrant than the cassia cinnamon you find in most American supermarkets, it had an incredibly intense, pungent aroma unlike any cinnamon I'd ever had before. I've never seen it in stores, but you can get it through mail order sources. Here I pair it with some of my favorite dessert flavorings: chocolate, coffee, and rum. If desired, you can freeze one of the layers to serve later.

4 ounces semisweet chocolate, roughly chopped
¾ pound (3 sticks) unsalted butter, cut into small pieces
¼ cup strong brewed coffee
¼ cup dark rum
2 cups sugar
3 large eggs
2 cups all-purpose flour
1 teaspoon ground cinnamon
⅛ teaspoon ground cloves
1 teaspoon baking powder
½ teaspoon baking soda
½ cup buttermilk
1 teaspoon vanilla extract
Cinnamon Whipped Cream (recipe follows)

Preheat the oven to 350°F. Butter and flour two 8-inch round cake pans, and set aside.

Combine the chocolate and butter in the top of a double boiler or a heatproof bowl set over gently simmering water, and stir frequently until melted. Remove from the heat. Stir in the coffee, rum, and sugar and stir until the sugar is dissolved.

Transfer to a large bowl and beat in the eggs, then stir in the flour, cinnamon, cloves, baking powder, and baking soda. Add the buttermilk and vanilla and mix until well combined and slightly thickened.

Pour the batter into the prepared pans. Bake until a toothpick or cake tester inserted in the center comes out clean, about 30 minutes. Remove from the oven and let cool in the pans on a wire rack for about 20 minutes.

Remove the cakes from the pans and let cool. Slice and serve with the whipped cream.

16 SERVINGS

CINNAMON WHIPPED CREAM

1 teaspoon ground cinnamon
1 cup heavy cream
¼ cup confectioners' sugar
1 teaspoon vanilla extract
2 tablespoons dark rum

Toast the cinnamon in a small sauté pan over medium heat until fragrant, 30 to 60 seconds. Remove from the heat and let cool.

Combine the cream, sugar, and vanilla in a large bowl and beat to semi-stiff peaks. Fold in the cinnamon and rum.

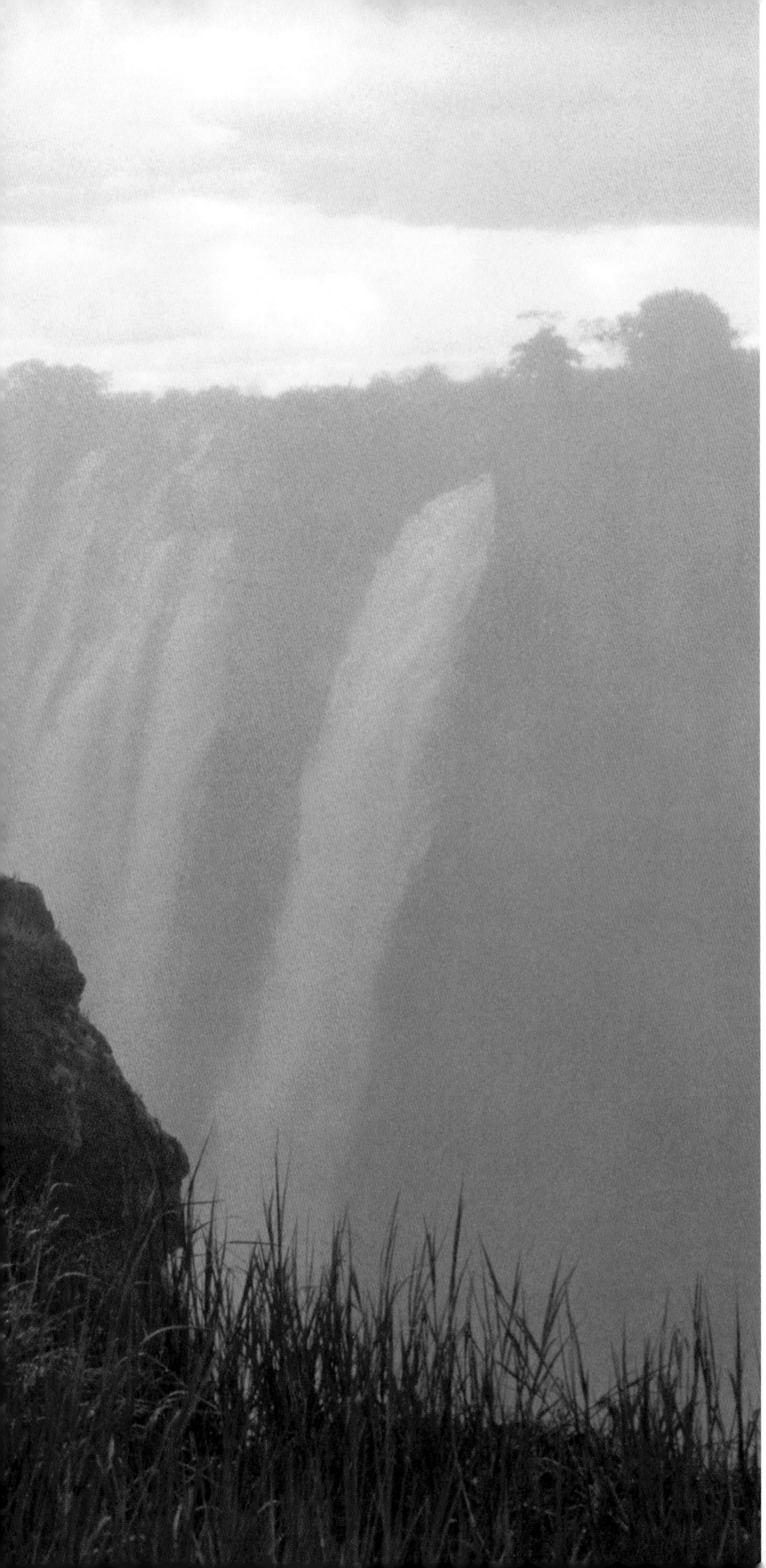

Happy
FATHER'S
DAY
QUENCH YOUR
THIRST
WITH POP
Better Quality
Better Quench
CHILDREN are not
to sit on the
COUNTER

GINGER-BANANA SALAD WITH HONEY ICE CREAM

The Bible refers to Ethiopia as the land of milk and honey, and to this day honey still plays an important part in the country's culinary repertoire: tej—the country's national drink—is a sweet wine made from honey, honey breads are commonly served, and Ethiopia is the world's tenth largest honey producer. The sweet, creamy ice cream in this recipe is inspired by the Ethiopian fondness for honey, and provides a silken contrast to the accompanying fruit salad.

½ cup packed brown sugar
One 1-inch piece ginger, peeled and thinly sliced
1 cinnamon stick
¾ cup water
Juice of 1 lemon
½ cup fresh orange juice
4 ripe bananas
Honey Ice Cream (recipe follows)

Combine the sugar, ginger, cinnamon stick, and water in a small saucepan and bring to a boil over high heat, stirring to dissolve the sugar. Remove from the heat and strain into a large bowl. Add the lemon juice and orange juice and chill for at least 1 hour.

Just before serving, slice the bananas on the diagonal into 1-inch pieces. Add them to the ginger syrup, turning to coat them well.

Serve the bananas with scoops of the ice cream, drizzling some ginger syrup over each serving.

6 SERVINGS

HONEY ICE CREAM

4 large egg yolks
¼ cup sugar, divided
1 cup heavy cream
1½ cups milk
⅓ cup honey

Whisk together the egg yolks and 2 tablespoons of the sugar in a small bowl until pale yellow and thick, about 5 minutes.

Combine the cream, milk, and the remaining 2 tablespoons sugar in a large saucepan and bring to a boil over medium heat, stirring to dissolve the sugar. Remove from the heat.

Whisking constantly, slowly add 1 cup of the hot milk mixture to the egg yolks (tempering the egg yolks this way keeps them from curdling or scrambling). Pour the egg mixture into the hot liquid and stir constantly over low heat until the custard coats the back of the spoon, about 5 minutes; do not allow to boil.

Meanwhile, fill a large bowl with ice water; set this ice bath aside.

Remove the custard from the heat and immediately strain it into a medium metal bowl. Nestle it in the ice bath and stir in the honey. Stir frequently until the custard is cool, then refrigerate for at least 2 hours.

Transfer the chilled custard to an ice cream maker and freeze according to the manufacturer's instructions. The ice cream will be soft and creamy. For a firmer consistency, transfer the ice cream to an airtight container and place in the freezer for at least 2 hours; remove from the freezer about 15 minutes before serving.

MAKES ABOUT 1 QUART

KOESISTERS

Cape Towners are justly proud of their koesisters, a doughnut that's a traditional after-church treat on Sundays. My search for the perfect koesister took me to the home of Peter and Marilyn Carelon, an energetic South African couple who run a printing business and a bed-and-breakfast from their home. They had two kinds of koesisters to share—a sweet, braided crullerlike pastry and a dark, round, spiced doughnut. Another version made without spices and dipped in a sugary syrup, known as koeksisters, is typically served in the homes of Afrikaners, but I was particularly fond of the spiced version, which featured notes of cinnamon, ginger, and cardamom.

6 tablespoons warm water
3 tablespoons granulated sugar
1 package active dry yeast (2¼ teaspoons)
2 cups all-purpose flour
1 teaspoon salt
3 extra-large egg yolks
5 tablespoons milk
2 tablespoons unsalted butter
¼ cup packed brown sugar
2 teaspoons ground cinnamon
1 teaspoon ground ginger
1 teaspoon ground cardamom, preferably freshly ground
About 4 cups canola oil for deep-frying

Combine the water, granulated sugar, and yeast in a large bowl and set in a warm place until the yeast begins to bubble, 5 to 10 minutes.

Add the flour and salt to the yeast and mix with an electric mixer on low speed until well combined. Beat in the egg yolks one at a time, beating after each addition until well incorporated.

Combine the milk and butter in a small saucepan and heat until butter is melted. With the mixer running, slowly pour the milk-butter mixture into the dough, beating until combined. Cover with a damp cloth or plastic wrap and let sit in a warm place until the dough doubles in size, about 40 minutes.

Punch the dough down and turn out onto a floured surface. Cut into 20 pieces, roll each one into a ball, and arrange in a single layer on a baking sheet. Set in a warm place and let rise for 20 minutes.

While the dough is rising, toss together the brown sugar, cinnamon, ginger, and cardamom in a large shallow bowl. Set aside.

Heat 3 inches of canola oil in a deep pot to 350°F. Working in batches, add the dough balls and fry, turning occasionally, until golden on all sides, about 3 to 4 minutes. Remove from the oil and drain on paper towels.

Toss the doughnuts in the mixed spices to coat. Serve warm.

MAKES 20 DOUGHNUTS

MALVA PUDDING

I first had this deliciously sticky, cakey steamed pudding at Eziko's, a cooking school and restaurant in the Cape Town township of Langa that serves a menu of traditional South African foods. It's a favorite throughout South Africa, and with good reason—it's homey and comforting, with familiar flavors that are easy to enjoy.

1 cup all-purpose flour
1 teaspoon baking soda
Pinch of salt
1¼ cups sugar, divided
1 egg
1 tablespoon unsalted butter, at room temperature, plus 8 tablespoons (1 stick) unsalted butter
¼ cup apricot jelly
1 cup milk
1 teaspoon white vinegar
1 teaspoon vanilla extract
1 cup evaporated milk
Whipped cream (optional)

Preheat the oven to 350°F. Sift together the flour, baking soda, and salt; set aside.

Beat together 1 cup of the sugar, the egg, the 1 tablespoon butter, and the jelly in a large bowl until pale and fluffy. Beat in the flour mixture.

Butter an 8-inch cake pan; set aside. Mix together the milk, vinegar, and vanilla in a small bowl, then fold into the egg mixture until thoroughly mixed. Pour into the buttered baking dish, and cover with lightly oiled foil.

Bake the pudding for about 30 minutes, until set. The cake will look spongy, with little holes dotting the top.

While the pudding is baking, combine the evaporated milk, the remaining 8 tablespoons butter, and the remaining ¼ cup sugar in a saucepan and heat, stirring, until the butter melts and the sugar has dissolved. Remove from the heat.

Pour the warm sauce slowly over the hot pudding and allow to stand for 10 minutes, or until all the liquid is absorbed. Serve warm with whipped cream.

4 SERVINGS

MANGO-PAPAYA KULFI

When the temperature soars, I can't think of anything more refreshing than kulfi—an Indian-style frozen dessert you find throughout East Africa. After a spicy-hot meal, it makes a great cooling accompaniment to fresh fruit or a slice of cake. You can even make kulfi popsicles, if you like; see the instructions below.

¾ cup sweetened condensed milk
1 cup heavy cream
¼ teaspoon ground cardamom, preferably freshly ground
1 cinnamon stick, broken in half
2 cups mango puree (see Note)
1 cup papaya puree (see Note)

16 popsicle sticks or wooden skewers (optional)

Combine the condensed milk, heavy cream, cardamom, cinnamon stick, mango puree, and papaya puree in a large bowl. Strain through a fine-mesh sieve into another bowl. Let stand at room temperature for 30 minutes.

Pour the mixture into sixteen 2-ounce paper cups and freeze until very thick but not hard, about 30 minutes. Insert the popsicle sticks, if using. Continue freezing until firm.

To serve, tear away the paper cups.

Note: If you can't find commercial mango puree or papaya puree at specialty markets or Caribbean grocery stores, you can make your own. Peel and pit 3 very ripe mangoes and puree in the food processor with 2 tablespoons sugar. Or puree 1 very ripe papaya, peeled and seeded, with 1 tablespoon sugar.

MAKES 16 PIECES

PEANUT CAKE WITH CARAMELIZED PAPAYAS AND PLUMS

roundnuts—what we know as peanuts in the United States—are eaten throughout West Africa at all meals and for all occasions. This rich, peanutty, rustic cake pays tribute to the humble groundnut, which is dressed up with a beautifully flavored topping of papayas and plums.

½ cup all-purpose flour
½ cup cornstarch
1 teaspoon baking soda
½ teaspoon ground cinnamon
¼ teaspoon ground nutmeg
½ cup unsalted peanuts
½ teaspoon salt
¼ cup peanut oil
1 cup milk
½ cup sugar
Caramelized Papayas and Plums (recipe follows)

Preheat the oven to 350°F. Generously butter an 8 x 4-inch loaf pan. Set aside. Whisk together the flour, cornstarch, baking soda, cinnamon, and nutmeg in a small bowl. Set aside.

Finely grind the peanuts with the salt in a food processor. Transfer to a medium bowl, add the oil, milk, and sugar, and stir until well combined. Add the dry ingredients and stir until well combined.

Pour the batter into the prepared pan. Bake for 35 to 40 minutes, or until a skewer inserted in the center comes out clean. Cool in the pan on a wire rack for 10 minutes, then invert the cake onto the rack and let cool for another 10 minutes.

To serve, cut the loaf into 1-inch slices and top with the papayas and plums.

7 TO 8 SERVINGS

CARAMELIZED PAPAYAS AND PLUMS

Juice of 2 lemons
½ cup water
½ cup sugar
1 vanilla bean
½ teaspoon ground cinnamon
1 papaya, peeled, seeded, and cut into ½-inch dice
4 large plums, pitted and cut into ½-inch dice
4 mint leaves, finely shredded

Bring the lemon juice and water to a boil in a medium saucepan. Add the sugar and stir to dissolve. With a sharp knife, split the vanilla bean lengthwise, then use the back of the knife to scrape out the seeds. Add the seeds, pod, and cinnamon to the pan, reduce the heat to a simmer, and simmer for 2 minutes. Add the papaya and plums, remove the pan from the heat, and let cool.

Remove the vanilla bean and discard. Fold in the mint.

PINEAPPLE-CASHEW SALAD

In tropical Africa, fresh fruits abound—pineapples, mangoes, oranges, mangosteens, bananas, passion fruit, and countless weird and wonderful fruits I'd never seen or heard of before. To me, fresh fruit is the perfect light, naturally sweet end to a meal. When you're looking for a way to cap off a barbecue or cookout, try this simple fruit salad, which combines pineapple chunks with cashews for a great texture that's dressed up with a dash of white wine and fresh mint.

½ cup sweet white wine, such as Riesling or ice wine
¼ cup packed brown sugar
½ golden pineapple, peeled, cored, and diced (about 1½ cups)
½ cup roasted cashews
4 mint leaves, finely shredded

Pour the wine into a medium bowl and add the sugar, stirring until it is dissolved. Add the pineapple cubes. Cover and refrigerate for 2 hours.

To serve, stir the cashews into the pineapple. Divide among serving bowls and sprinkle with the mint.

6 SERVINGS

SESAME COOKIES

I always associated sesame seeds with Japanese and Chinese cooking, so I was surprised to learn that the sesame plant originated in West Africa and spread throughout the continent in ancient times. In fact, I found out, sesame seeds were cultivated by the ancient Egyptians, and the very name derives from the Egyptian word "sesemt." Sesame seeds are still prevalent in the cooking of Africa, where they are used in spice rubs, like za'atar, or in desserts, like this sesame cookie. Toasting the sesame seeds until they are slightly fragrant—about 30 seconds—will intensify their flavor, but be sure not to overcook them because the oil in the seeds will burn quickly.

½ cup plus 2 tablespoons all-purpose flour
½ teaspoon baking powder
½ teaspoon salt
4 tablespoons (½ stick) unsalted butter
1 cup packed light brown sugar
1 large egg
½ teaspoon vanilla extract
1 teaspoon fresh lemon juice
1 cup sesame seeds, toasted

Combine the flour, baking powder, and salt in a small bowl; set aside.

Using an electric stand mixer or hand mixer, cream the butter and brown sugar in a large bowl until light and fluffy. Add the egg, vanilla, and lemon juice and beat until thoroughly blended, about 30 seconds. On low speed, slowly add the flour mixture and mix just until incorporated. Beat in the sesame seeds. Allow the dough to rest, covered, in the refrigerator for 1 hour.

Preheat the oven to 350°F. Line two baking sheets with parchment paper and grease the parchment (or use Silpat liners). Drop the dough by heaping teaspoons onto the baking sheets, leaving about 1½ inches between cookies.

Bake the cookies until golden, about 5 to 7 minutes, turning the baking sheets around midway through baking. Remove from the baking sheets and cool on a wire rack.

MAKES 3 DOZEN COOKIES

SOUR TAMARIND-ALMOND BALLS

My friend Kingsley is from Saint Lucia, and when his mother comes to visit she treats us to a feast of African-influenced Caribbean favorites. These tamarind-almond balls are one of her specialties—she makes them with fresh tamarind, which she kneads into a paste and wraps around a piece of almond. The result is a wonderfully tart and sour snack you can pop into your mouth like candy. I've adapted her recipe, using tamarind paste in place of the fresh fruit, which can be difficult to find. Look for tamarind paste at ethnic grocery stores or specialty shops. If you find these a little too tart for your taste, roll the balls in powdered sugar.

2 tablespoons (about 10 to 12) blanched whole almonds
Juice of 2 limes
5 tablespoons sugar
½ teaspoon ground ginger
½ teaspoon freshly ground black pepper
1 tablespoon dark rum
1 teaspoon vanilla extract
1½ cups tamarind paste (see pages 5-6)

Toast the almonds in a small sauté pan over high heat until golden, about 2 to 3 minutes. Remove from the heat and let cool slightly, then cut in half. Set aside.

Combine the lime juice and sugar in a small saucepan and bring to a boil, stirring to dissolve the sugar. Remove from the heat and add the ginger, black pepper, rum, and vanilla.

Place the tamarind paste in a bowl, add the lime juice mixture a little at a time, and knead until the liquid is incorporated. Wrap about 2 teaspoons of tamarind paste around each almond and roll into a ball.

MAKES ABOUT 20 PIECES

TANGERINE CONSOMMÉ WITH TAPIOCA

Most Americans would say they've never tasted cassava, a staple vegetable of West African cooking. But if you've ever eaten tapioca, you've had this ubiquitous root vegetable. Tapioca is derived from cassava, and I like to use it to add a pearly texture to desserts like panna cottas or fruit soups. The first time you have tapioca, the texture can be surprising—but it's a taste that's easy to acquire because it's so interesting. It doesn't have much flavor on its own, so you have to cook it with a flavorful liquid; here I use coconut milk to give the tapioca pearls a rich, full taste, and mix it with some of my favorite fruits. You can use whatever fresh fruits are in season—I call for my favorites, mango, papaya, and raspberries—but you can experiment with passion fruit, blueberries, or the fruits you like best in this refreshing dessert, which plays off the African tradition of ending a meal with fruit.

1 vanilla bean
1 cup sugar, divided
2 lemongrass stalks, sliced
Grated zest and juice of 2 lemons
1 cup water
½ cup small pearl tapioca, soaked overnight in 3 cups water
One 15-ounce can coconut milk
1 cup diced mango
1 cup diced papaya
½ cup raspberries
6 mint leaves, finely shredded
2 cups fresh tangerine juice

With a sharp knife, split the vanilla bean lengthwise, then use the back of the knife to scrape out the seeds. Combine the vanilla seeds, ½ cup of the sugar, the lemongrass, lemon zest, and water in a small saucepan and bring to a boil over high heat. Remove from the heat and let cool, then refrigerate for 30 minutes, or until chilled.

Combine the tapioca and any remaining liquid, the coconut milk, and the remaining ½ cup sugar in a saucepan and bring to a boil. Reduce the heat to low and simmer for 10 minutes, or until the tapioca pearls are tender and translucent. Remove from the heat and let cool.

Stir the mango, papaya, and raspberries into the tapioca and fold in the mint. Set aside.

Strain the chilled lemon syrup into a bowl. Stir in the tangerine juice and lemon juice.

To serve, divide the tapioca among six shallow soup bowls, and pour the consommé around the tapioca.

6 SERVINGS

SWEET POTATO–COCONUT TURNOVERS

I love using root vegetables in desserts—whether it's beets, carrots, or sweet potatoes, these hearty, filling vegetables lend a great, slightly unexpected taste and richness to traditional desserts. Here, I use sweet potatoes as the base of a flaky turnover crust that's stuffed with coconut, a common flavor in sub-Saharan countries.

2 medium sweet potatoes, peeled
3 to 4 cups all-purpose flour
½ cup sugar
½ teaspoon salt
Coconut Filling (recipe follows)
8 tablespoons (1 stick) unsalted butter, or as needed, divided
1 cup sour cream
2 tablespoons confectioners' sugar
Juice of 1 lime

To make the dough, cook the sweet potatoes in a saucepan of boiling water until tender. Drain, then press through a potato ricer into a large bowl. Stir in 3 cups flour, the sugar, and salt, mixing well, then turn out on a floured work surface and knead, adding as much of the remaining cup of flour as necessary to achieve a smooth, workable dough. Wrap in plastic and set aside to rest for at least 30 minutes.

Divide the dough into 12 equal pieces, and roll each piece into a ball. One at a time, on a lightly floured surface, roll each piece into a 6-inch circle. Place 1½ tablespoons of the filling in the center, use your fingertips to brush a little water around the outer edge of the circle, and then carefully fold the dough in half. Crimp the edges with your fingers or a fork to seal.

Melt 2 tablespoons of the butter on a griddle or in a skillet over medium heat. Add 2 or 3 turnovers and fry until golden on the bottom, about 3 minutes. Turn and fry the other side, then transfer to paper towels to drain. Fry the remaining turnovers, adding more butter as needed. Let cool.

Place the sour cream in a small bowl and whisk in the confectioners' sugar and lime juice. Place a dollop of the sour cream mixture on each turnover before serving.

MAKES 12 TURNOVERS

COCONUT FILLING

1 cup thawed frozen grated coconut or sweetened shredded coconut
⅓ cup packed dark brown sugar
¼ cup chopped toasted cashews
½ cup golden raisins
2 tablespoons sesame seeds, toasted

Combine all the ingredients in a medium bowl and mix until well combined.

GINGER BEER

One afternoon in Johannesburg, I met an incredibly driven young woman. Her ambition: to bottle and market her family's traditional gemmer (ginger beer) recipe. When I tasted her concoction, I could see why she was convinced she would succeed—it was sweet, frothy, and gingery, with a great balance of flavor, and incredibly invigorating. She refused to reveal her family's secret ingredients, but I've reproduced the flavor as closely as I can here. Enjoy it on a hot day, when you need a refreshing beverage to get you going.

Juice of 4 limes
1 cup orange juice
4 cups water
Two 3-inch pieces ginger, peeled and coarsely grated
½ cup sugar
4 cloves
4 cardamom pods

Combine the limes, orange juice, water, ginger, sugar, cloves, and cardamom in a large saucepan and bring to a boil. Pour into a bowl, and let cool.

Cover and refrigerate the ginger beer for at least 2 hours or up to 1 day. Strain before serving.

4 TO 6 SERVINGS

MINT ICED TEA

In Morocco, guests are greeted with a steaming cup of green tea flavored with mint and lots and lots of sugar. Traditionally it is served hot, but chilled it makes a refreshing and thirst-quenching beverage that's perfect with a hot and spicy meal.

4 cups water
2 tablespoons sugar
2 tablespoons honey
6 mint sprigs
One 3-inch piece ginger, peeled and sliced
4 teaspoons green tea leaves
1 lemon, cut into quarters

Combine the water, sugar, honey, mint sprigs, and ginger in a large saucepan and bring to a boil, then reduce the heat and simmer for 5 minutes. Add the green tea and simmer for another 3 minutes. Strain and let cool.

Serve the tea over ice cubes, garnished with the lemon.

4 SERVINGS

LEMONGRASS TISANE

This rejuvenating infusion is made with lemongrass, a popular flavoring in sub-Saharan Africa. Hot teas and tisanes—they are rarely served iced—are a popular beverage all over the continent, usually served with copious amounts of milk and sugar.

6 cups water
2 stalks lemongrass, coarsely chopped
Milk and sugar for serving

Bring the water to a boil in a medium saucepan. Add the lemongrass, remove from the heat, cover, and let steep for 15 minutes.

Strain the tisane through a fine-mesh sieve, and pour into teacups. Serve with milk and sugar.

6 SERVINGS

TAMARIND DRINK

The sour, pulpy fruit of the tamarind tree grows in pods, the flesh clinging to tiny beans at the core. Native to Africa, tamarind has spread to India, Southeast Asia, Latin America, and the Caribbean, where it's become an important part of regional cooking. I was surprised to learn that tamarind is also an important ingredient in a condiment that's used around the world—Worcestershire sauce.

Tamarind is very tart. If desired, add more honey or sugar to the beverage to taste, as you would with iced tea.

7 cups water
1 cup tamarind pulp
¼ cup honey

Bring the water to a boil in a large saucepan. Add the tamarind pulp and honey and stir until dissolved. Strain and chill.

Serve over ice.

8 SERVINGS

SOURCES

Whenever possible, I adapted the recipes in this book to substitute easier-to-find ingredients for African spices, meats, vegetables, and other foods. But in some cases, nothing but the original will do. Most large cities in North America have at least one African market where you can find all sorts of interesting and wonderful ingredients, like sumac, morning glory, dried fish and meats, and ready-to-make fufu or ugali. You can also check out Asian, Caribbean, Latin, Indian, and Middle Eastern markets, which carry a variety of spices and vegetables you can't find at traditional grocery stores. And don't overlook local African restaurants; often the proprietor will be willing to sell regular customers the ingredients they need. For those really hard-to-find items, the Internet is a great resource; I've listed a few of my favorite sites below.

AA BILTONG

Fullwood Plaza
11229 East Independence Boulevard
(Highway 74)
Matthews, NC 28105
888-532-1433
www.lekker.freeservers.com
Biltong, boerewors, and other South African specialties

ALWAYSFRESHFISH.COM

1889 Highway 9, Unit 41
Toms River, NJ 08755
732-349-0518
www.alwaysfreshfish.com
Fresh and frozen seafood, including crayfish, shrimp, lobster, and more

D'ARTAGNAN

280 Wilson Avenue
Newark, NJ 07105
800-DARTAGNAN (327-8246);
973-344-0456
www.dartagnan.com
Foie gras, sausages, smoked delicacies, venison, and organic game and poultry

ETHIOPIANSPICES.COM

3315 Bardstown Road
Louisville, KY 40218
www.ethiopianspices.com
Ethiopian spices and spice blends, shiro, teff, coffee beans, and fresh injera

FRIEDA'S INC.

4465 Corporate Center Drive
Los Alamitos, CA 90720-2561
800-241-1771
www.friedas.com
Exotic fruits and vegetables, fresh and dried chilies

KALUSTYAN'S

123 Lexington Avenue
New York, NY 10016
212-685-3451
www.kalustyans.com
Bulk spices, herbs, teas, coffee, legumes, rice, nuts and seeds, oils, pickles, preserves, banana leaves, chilies, tamarind paste, and many other international ingredients

PENZEY'S SPICES

19300 Janacek Court
Brookfield, WI 53045
800-741-7787
www.penzeys.com
Bulk spices, seasonings, herbs, and spice blends

T SALON AND EMPORIUM

11 East 20th Street
New York, NY 10003
212-358-0506
www.tsalon.com
Teas from around the globe, including South African rooibios blends

WORLD MERCHANTS

1509 Western Avenue
Seattle, WA 98101
206-682-7274
www.worldspice.com
Spices and spice blends, herbs, dried chilies, and teas

INDEX

A

Abbe (author's friend), 123
Abdullah (author's friend), 209
Africa, about, xi–xii, xvii–xxiii. *See also* East Africa; North Africa; South Africa; West Africa; Traveling in Africa
Almonds
  Almond Cookies, 302
  Almond Sambal, 65
  in Dried Fruit Bread, 143
  Roasted Veal Shanks with Apricots and Almonds, 294
  Sour Tamarind-Almond Balls, 329
Apple-Squash Fritters, 172
Apricots
  dried, in Dried Fruit Bread, 143
  roasted veal shanks with, and almonds, 294
Aquavit, 77, 114, 293
Asefa, Mesfin, xi
Asfaw, Muluwork, 249–251
Avocado
  Avocado Fool, 303
  Avocado Pap, 89
  Cassava-Avocado Mash, 92
  Couscous-Avocado Salad, 215
  Crispy Avocado, 95
  in Crispy Vegetables, 182
  Grilled Tilapia-Avocado Soup, 122
Awase, 14
Ayib. *See* Fresh Cheese with Chives

B

Baccalao. *See* Warm Potato-Cod Salad
Baguette, fried fish, 163
Bahama Spice Farm, Tanzania, traveling in, 20–25
Balls, sour tamarind-almond, 329
Banana(s)
  Banana Fritters, 304, 305
  Bananas Flambé, 315
  Ginger-Banana Salad, 321
Banana leaves, about, 1
  snapper wrapped in, 230, 231
Barbecued Oxtail, 272
Barbecued Pork Ribs, 270, 271
Barbecued Roast Beef with Plum Sauce, 273
Barbecued Snapper, 202
Barbecue Sauce, 44
Bass dishes
  Chermoula-Roasted Bass, 204, 205
  Fried Fish Baguette, 163
  in Seafood and Rice, 224, 225
  Spiced Bass with Crunchy Rice and Watercress Salad, 232, 233
Batter, beer, 93
Beans, about, 1
  fava, in Sautéed Vegetable, 193
  vanilla, about, 6
  white, and sardine salad, 88
  white, puree, 72
Beef
  Barbecued Roast Beef with Plum Sauce, 273
  Boharat Beef Skewers, 282
  ground, in Bobotie, 285
  ground, in Boerewors Sausage Patties, 281
  ground, in Kofta Meatballs with Okra Tomato Sauce, 284
  in Steak Tartare, 294
  Stir-Fried Beef Stew, 130, 131
Beer, ginger, 333
Beer Batter, 93
Beets
  in Beet-Ginger Chutney, 47
  in Sautéed Vegetables, 193
  in Vegetable Tagine, 196
Berbere, 12, 13
Berbere-Crusted Rack of Lamb, 274
Bissap Granité, 306, 307
Black beans
  in Crab Burgers, 154, 155
  in Grilled Tilapia-Avocado Soup, 122
Black-Eyed Peas, 173
Black Olive Oil, 15
Bobotie, 285
Boerewors Sausage Patties, 281
Boharat, 17
Boharat Beef Skewers, 282
Boil, crayfish, spicy, 126
Bok choy, as substitute in Sautéed Morning Glory, 192
Braai, about, 273
  Cumin Braai Bread, 141
Branson, Richard, 118
Breads. *See also* Flatbreads; Sandwiches
  Corn Bread, 140
  Cumin Braai Bread, 141
  Curry Chapatis, 142
  Dried Fruit Bread, 143
  Honey Bread, 150
  Injera, *144*, 145
  Pita Bread, 151
  Roti, 152
  Toasted Peanut Bread, 153
  Toasted Spiced Dried Fruit Bread, 254
Brown sugar, about 1
Bulgur, about, 1
Burgers, crab, 154, 155
Butter
  clarified, about, 2
  peanut, 313
  spiced, 34

C

Cabbage dishes
  Citrus Cabbage Salad, 77
  Pickled Cabbage, 98
  Warm Cabbage, 197
  in Zanzibari "Pizzas", 166
Café Parisian (Addis Ababa) 139
Cakes
  Chocolate Rum Cake with Cinnamon Whipped Cream, 316, 317
  Peanut Cake, 326
Callaloo, 112
Candied Yams and Plantains, *174*, 175

Cape Town (South Africa), xxi, 83, 138, 164, 308–312, 324
Caramelized Mango Soup with Poppy Seed Rice Pudding, 314
Caramelized Papayas and Plums, 326
Cardamom, about, 1
Carelon, Marilyn, 141, 322
Carelon, Peter, 141, 322
Carim, Gadijah, 310–312
Cashew, pineapple-, salad, 327
Cassava, about, 1
  Cassava-Avocado Mash, 92
  Cassava-Stuffed Shrimp, 203
  in Chicken Mofongo, 243
  in Crispy Vegetables, 182
Casserole. *See* Bobotie
Catfish, fried, 214
Cauliflower Fritters, 93
Chapatis
  curry, 142
  spicy tuna on, 167
Char with Sakay, 206
Chase, Leah, 214
Cheese, fresh, with chives, 52
Chermoula, 15
Chermoula-Roasted Bass, *204*, 205
Chicken
  about, 240–242
  Chicken and Shrimp Soup, 113
  Chicken Mofongo, 243
  Chicken-Peanut Stew, 114
  Chicken Stew (Doro Wett), *244*, 245
  ground, in Merguez Sausage, 293
  Jerk Chicken, *260*, 261
  in Jollof Rice, 265
  Lemon-Olive Chicken, 262, 263
Chickpeas, about, 2
  Chickpea-Eggplant Dip, 42, 43
  in Crispy Vegetables, 182
  in Falafel with Quick Tomato Sauce, 184, *185*
Chilies, about, 2
  Chili-Spiced Lamb Sandwiches, 158
  Coconut-Chili Sauce, 207
  Rum-Pickled Chilies, 60
Chili Mayonnaise, 45
Chives, fresh cheese with, 52
Chocolate, about, 2
  Chocolate-Coconut Sorbet with Peanut Butter, 313
  Chocolate Pancakes with Bananas Flambé, 315
  Chocolate Rum Cake with Cinnamon Whipped Cream, 316, *317*
  in Dried Fruit Bread, 143
Chunky Mashed Vegetables, 176
Chutneys
  beet-ginger, 47
  foie gras–date, 254
  plantain, 48
  quince, 49
Cinnamon, about, 2
Cinnamon Whipped Cream, 316, *317*
Citrus Cabbage Salad, 77
Citrus peel, preserved, 58, 59
Clams
  in Malata, 216, *217*
  in Seafood and Rice, *224*, 225
Clare (author's friend), 122, 191, 282
Clarified butter, about, 2
Clinton, Bill, 118
Coconut dishes
  Chocolate-Coconut Sorbet, 313
  Coconut Filling, 332
  Coconut-chili sauce, curried trout with, 207
  Plantain-Coconut Stew, 124
  Sweet Potato–Coconut Turnovers, 332
Coconut milk, about, 2
Cod
  Cod Stew with Sesame Seeds, 120, *121*
  in Grilled Seafood Salad with Yogurt Sauce, 79
  as substitute in Rice-Crusted Hake, 219
  Warm Potato-Cod Salad, 87
Coffee, about, 3
Coffee grinder, about, 7
Condensed milk, about, 3
Condiments. *See also* Dips; Sambals; Sauces; Side dishes
  Preserved Citrus Peel, 58, 59
  Rum-Pickled Chilies, 60
  Tamarind Vinaigrette, 66
  Tarragon Mustard, 67
  Thyme-Roasted Garlic, 68, 69
  Tomato Date Jam, 70
Consommé, tangerine, with tapioca, 330, 331
Cookies
  almond, 302
  sesame, 328
Corn
  in Chicken and Shrimp Soup, 113
  Corn Bread, 140
  Corn Mashed Potatoes, 94
  in Guinea Hen with Shiro, 255
  Mustard Greens and Corn, 183
  Squid with Corn-Tomato Soup, 128, *129*
Cornmeal, about, 3
  porridge. *See* Avocado Pap
Couscous, about, 3
  Couscous-Avocado Salad, 215
  Mango Couscous, 96, 97
Crab
  Crab Burgers, 154, *155*
  Crab Soup, 115
  in Spicy Crayfish Boil, 126
Crayfish boil, spicy, 126
Cream, whipped, cinnamon, 316, *317*
Creamed Swiss Chard, 177
Crispy Avocado, 95
Crispy Vegetables, 182
Cucumber
  Cucumber Salad, 78
  Cucumber Sambal, 65
  Tomato-Cucumber Salad, *160*, 161
Cumin Braai Bread, 141
Curried dishes
  Curried Trout with Coconut-Chili Sauce, 207
  Curry Chapatis, 142
  Green Curry Paste, 26
  Lamb Curry, 288

D

Dar es Salaam, Tanzania, traveling in, 82–85
Dark-Spiced Turkey Legs, 252
Dark Spice Mix, 18

Date(s)
in Dried Fruit Bread, 143
Foie Gras–Date Chutney, 254
Tomato Date Jam, 70
Desserts, 299–335
Dips
Chickpea-Eggplant Dip, 42, 43
Chili Mayonnaise, 45
Yogurt Dip, 73
District Six, Cape Town, South Africa, traveling in, 308–312
Donovan (author's friend), 261
Doro Wett, 245
Doughnuts, 310–312. *See* Koesisters
Dried Fruit Bread, 143
toasted spiced, 254
Drinks
Bissap Granité, 306, 307
Ginger Beer, 333
Lemongrass Tisane, 334
Mint Iced Tea, 333
Tamarind Drink, 334
Duck breasts, Moroccan-style, 264
Duck Skewers, 246, 247
Dumplings
Potato-Lentil Dumplings, 162
Vegetable Samosas, 165, 166
Duqqa, 19
Duqqa-Cured Venison Loin, 297
Dutch East India Company, 309

E

East Africa, xx, 12, 14, 20–25, 26, 34, 40, 47, 52, 53, 76, 82–85, 89, 103, 105, 111, 122, 123, 127, 131, 134, 138–139, 142, 145, 146–149, 150, 152, 163, 166, 176, 178–181, 191, 197, 200, 207, 215, 234, 236, 240, 245, 246, 248–250, 255, 268–269, 274, 282, 289, 295, 300, 316, 321, 325
Egg(s)
Egg Sandwiches, 159
Spiced Egg Salad, 81
Eggplant
Chickpea-Eggplant Dip, 42, 43
in Crispy Vegetables, 182
Roasted Eggplant and Plantains, 191
Warm Eggplant–Butternut Squash Salad, 86
in Vegetable Tagine, 196
Egyptian-Style Salted Squab, 253
Ephrem, Yeworkwoha "Workye", 249
Equipment, about, 7
Eziko's (Cape Town), 83, 324

F

Falafel with Quick Tomato Sauce, 184, 185
Fenugreek seeds, about, 3
Filling
coconut, 332
potato-lentil, 162
vegetable, 165
Fish. *See specific types*
Flambé, bananas, 315
Flatbreads
Curry Chapatis, 142
Injera, *144*, 145
Spicy Tuna on Chapatis, 167
Zanzibari "Pizzas", 166
Foie gras
Foie Gras–Date Chutney with Toasted Spiced Dried Fruit Bread, 254
Quail–Foie Gras Soup, 125
Fool, avocado, 303
Fresh Cheese with Chives, 52
Fried Catfish, 214
Fried Fish Baguette, 163
Friedrich, Marc, 309
Fritters
apple-squash, 172
banana, 304, 305
cauliflower, 93
Fruit. *See also specific fruits*
Dried Fruit Bread, 143
in Preserved Citrus Peel, 58, 59
Fruit salads
Ginger-Banana Salad, 321
Pineapple-Cashew Salad, 327
Fufu, about, 84. *See also* Cassava-Avocado Mash; Corn Mashed Potatoes

G

Garlic, thyme-roasted, 68, 69
Gediyon (author's friend), 147–148
Ginger-Banana Salad with Honey Ice Cream, 321
Ginger Beer, 333
Ginger Paste, 26
Ginger, beet-, chutney, 47
Granité, bissap, 306, 307
Green Curry Paste, 26
Green Masala, 27
Grilled Seafood Salad with Yogurt Sauce, 79
Grilled Tilapia-Avocado Soup, 122
Grinder, spice or coffee, about, 7
Guinea Hen with Shiro, 255

H

Hake
in Grilled Seafood Salad with Yogurt Sauce, 79
rice-crusted, 219
Hamid (author's friend), 86
Harissa, 30
Harissa-Roasted Turkey Breast, 256
Harris, Jessica, xii, xxi
Hen, guinea, with shiro, 255
Herring-Potato Salad, 80
Honey Bread, 150
Honey Ice Cream, 321
Hummus. *See* Chickpea-Eggplant Dip; White Bean Puree

I

Ice cream, honey, 321
Ile de Goree, 315
Ingredients, about, 1–6
Injera, *144*, 145

J

Jam, tomato date, 70
Janse, Margot, 218
Jerk Chicken, 260, 261
Jerk Mix, 31

J'mal Fna, Marrakech, Morocco, traveling in, 62–63
Jollof Rice, 265
Jones, Quincy, 118
Juilles, Owen, 309–310

K

Kale, in Lamb Stir-Fry, 289
Kefta, lamb and veal, *160*, 1 61
Keke (author's friend), 173
Ketchup, papaya, 53
Khan el-Khalili, 253
Khayelitsha, South Africa, traveling in, 276–279
Kingsley (author's friend), 162, 223, 272, 329
Koesisters, 322, 323
  about, 310–312
Kofta Meatballs with Okra Tomato Sauce, 284
Kulfi, mango-papaya, 325

L

Lamb
  Berbere-Crusted Rack of Lamb, 274
  Chili-Spiced Lamb Sandwiches, 58
  ground, in Boerewors Sausage Patties, 281
  ground, in Kofta Meatballs with Okra Tomato Sauce, 284
  ground, in Lamb-Stuffed Tomatoes, 290
  ground, in Merguez Sausage, 292, 293
  Lamb and Veal Kefta with Tomato-Cucumber Salad, *160*, 161
  Lamb Curry, 288
  Lamb Stir-Fry, 289
  Za'atar-Roasted Leg of Lamb, 296
Lemongrass, about, 3
Lemongrass Tisane, 334, 335
Lemon-Olive Chicken, 262, 263
Lentils, about, 3–4
  Potato-Lentil Dumplings, 162
  Potato-Lentil Filling, 162
  Lentil Stew, 123
Liver, goose. *See* Foie gras
Lobster Skewers with Couscous-Avocado Salad, 215

M

Malata, 216, *217*
Malva Pudding, 324
Mandela, Nelson, 117, 119, 277
Mandoline, about, 7
Mango, about, 4
  Caramelized Mango Soup, 314
  Mango Couscous, 96, 97
  Mango Sambal, 64
  Mango-Papaya Kulfi, 325
  in Tangerine Consommé with Tapioca, 330, 331
Marc's Mediterranean Cooking (South Africa), 309
Masala, green, 27
Mash
  cassava-avocado, 92
  pumpkin, *186*, 187
Mashed potatoes, corn, 94
Mayonnaise, chili, 45
Meatballs, kofta, 284
Meat dishes, 267–297. *See also specific types*
  ground meat, in Zanzibari "Pizzas", 166
Merguez Sausage, 292, 293
  about, 4
  in Cassava-Stuffed Shrimp, 203
  in Shiro-Stuffed Tomatoes, 104
Merkata, Addis Ababa, Ethiopia, traveling in, 178–181
Meze. *See* Warm Eggplant–Butternut Squash Salad
Milk
  coconut, about, 2
  condensed, about, 3
Mint Iced Tea, 333
Mix
  dark spice, 18
  jerk, 31
Mofongo, chicken, 243
Morning glory, about, 4
  sautéed, 192
  in Snapper Wrapped in Banana Leaves, 230, 231
Moroccan-Style Duck Breasts, 264
Mortar and pestle, about, 7
Muna (author's friend), 96
Mussels, in Seafood and Rice, 224, 225
Mustard, tarragon, 67
Mustard Greens and Corn, 183

N

Ndaba, Wandie, 117–119
Nit'ir qibe. *See* Spiced Butter
North Africa, xviii–xix, 15, 17, 30, 32, 35, 37, 41, 42, 57, 59, 62–63, 76, 86, 96, 102, 120, 138, 158, 161, 184, 196, 200, 240–241, 253, 254, 256, 263, 264, 268, 284, 290, 293, 294, 296, 300–301, 302, 333
Nshima. *See* Avocado Pap
Ntozini, Piksteel, 277–278
Ntozini, Vicky, 277

O

Okra, about, 4
  in Chicken and Shrimp Soup, 113
  in Crab Soup, 115
  Okra Tomato Sauce, 284
  Spicy Okra, 194, 195
Olive, lemon-, chicken, 263
Olive oil, black, 15
Onions, pickled, 55
Oxtail, barbecued, 272
Oysters with Green Tomato Water, 218

P

Palaver Sauce, 190
Palm oil, about, 4
Pancakes, chocolate, 315
Pap, avocado, 89
Papayas, about, 4
  Caramelized Papayas and Plums, 326
  Mango-Papaya Kulfi, 325
  Papaya Ketchup, 53

Pickled Green and Yellow Papayas, 54
in Tangerine Consommé with Tapioca, 330, 331
Parsnips
in Jerk Chicken, 260, 261
in Stuffing, 256
in Vegetable Tagine, 196
Pasta dishes
Red Penne, 102
Trout Spaghetti, 234, 235
Paste
ginger, 26
green curry, 26
Peacock Hotel, 83
Peanuts, about, 5
Chicken-Peanut Stew, 114
in Citrus Cabbage Salad, 77
Peanut Butter, 313
Peanut Cake with Caramelized Papayas and Plums, 326
in Squid with Corn-Tomato Soup, 128, *129*
Toasted Peanut Bread, 153
Peas, black-eyed, 173
Penne, red, 102
Pickled, rum-, chilies, 60
Pickled Cabbage, 98
Pickled Green and Yellow Papayas, 54
Pickled Onions, 55
Pineapple-Cashew Salad, 327
Piri Piri, 56
Shrimp Piri Piri, 228, 229
Pistachio Rouille, 57
Pita Bread, 151
"Pizzas," Zanzibari, 166
Plantains, about, 5
Candied Yams and Plantains, 174, 175
in Crispy Vegetables, 182
Plantain Chutney, 48
Plantain-Coconut Stew, 124
Plantain-Crusted Yellowtail, 222
Roasted Eggplant and Plantains, 191
in Snapper Wrapped in Banana Leaves, 230, 231
Spicy Plantain Chips, 106, *107*
Plums
Caramelized Papayas and Plums, 326
Plum Sauce, 273
Pomegranate Rice, 99
Poppy Seed Rice Pudding, 314
Pork ribs, barbecued, 270, 271
Potato(es). *See also* Sweet potatoes
Corn Mashed Potatoes, 94
Herring-Potato Salad, 80
in Jerk Chicken, 260, 261
Potato-Lentil Dumplings, 162
Potato-Lentil Filling, 162
in Pumpkin Mash, 186, 187
in Red Penne, 102
in Sautéed Vegetables, 193
in Spicy Crayfish Boil, 126
in Vegetable Tagine, 196
Warm Potato-Cod Salad, 87
in White Bean–Sardine Salad, 88
Poultry. *See specific types*
how to cut up chicken, 242
how to truss a bird, 242
Preserved Citrus Peel, 58, 59
Pudding
malva, 324
rice, poppy seed, 314
Pumpkin Mash, *186*, 187
Puree, white bean, 72

Q

Qa'b el-ghazal, 302
Quail–Foie Gras Soup, 125
Le Quartier FranÁais, 218
Quince
in Jerk Chicken, 260, 261
Quince Chutney, 49
in Stuffing, 256

R

Ras Al-Hanout, 32
Raspberries, in Tangerine Consommé with Tapioca, 330, 331
Red Penne, 102
Red Rice, *100*, 101
Rice dishes
about, 5
Crunchy Rice and Watercress Salad, 232, 233
Jollof Rice, 265
Pomegranate Rice, 99
Red Rice, *100*, 101
Rice-Crusted Hake, 219
Seafood and Rice, *224*, 225
in Snapper Wrapped in Banana Leaves, 230, 231
in Spicy Tilapia Stew, 127
Yellow Rice, 105
Rice pudding, poppy seed, 314
Roast beef, barbecued, 273
Roasted Eggplant and Plantains, 191
Roasted Veal Shanks with Apricots and Almonds, 294
Rooibos, about, 291
Roti, 152
Rouille, pistachio, 57
Rub, yogurt, 35
Rum cake, chocolate, 316, 317
Rum-Pickled Chilies, 60

S

Sakay, 61
char with, 206
Salads. *See also* Fruit salads
Citrus Cabbage Salad, 77
Couscous-Avocado Salad, 215
Crunchy Rice and Watercress Salad, 232, 233
Cucumber Salad, 78
Grilled Seafood Salad with Yogurt Sauce, 79
Pickled Cabbage, 98
Tomato-Cucumber Salad, *160*, 161
Warm Eggplant–Butternut Squash Salad, 86
Warm Potato-Cod Salad, 87
White Bean–Sardine Salad, 88
Salmon Skewers with Tamarind Sauce, 223
Sambal
almond, 65
cucumber, 65
mango, 64

Samosas, vegetable, 165, *166*
Samuelsson, Ann Marie (mother), xi
Samuelsson, Lennart (father), xi
Samuelsson, Linda Fantye (sister), xi
Samuelsson, Marcus (Kasshun Tsegie), background, xi–xii,
Sandwiches
 Chili-Spiced Lamb Sandwiches, 158
 Crab Burgers, 154, *155*
 Egg Sandwiches, 159
 Fried Fish Baguette, 163
 Lamb and Veal Kefta with Tomato-Cucumber Salad, *160*, 161
Sardine
 in Citrus Cabbage Salad, 77
 in Cucumber Salad, 78
 White Bean–Sardine Salad, 88
Sauces
 barbecue, 44
 coconut-chili, curried trout with, 207
 palaver, 190
 Papaya Ketchup, 53
 Piri Piri
 Pistachio Rouille, 57
 plum, 273
 Sakay, 61
 spinach, trout with, 134
 tamarind, salmon skewers with, 223
 tomato, 71
 tomato, okra, 284
 tomato, quick, falafel with, 184, *185*
 yogurt, 79
Sausage
 boerewors, patties, 281
 merguez. *See* Merguez Sausage
Sautéed Morning Glory, 192
Sautéed Vegetables, 193
Seafood. *See also specific types*
 Grilled Seafood Salad, 79
 Seafood and Rice, *224*, 225
Seared Cured Yellowtail, 226, *227*
Sesame Cookies, 328
Sesame seeds
 cod stew with, 120, *121*
 in Duqqa, 19
 in Za'atar, 37
Shark, tomato-roasted, 237
Shiro, 103
 guinea hen with, 255
 Shiro-Stuffed Tomatoes, 104
Shiro powder, about, 5
Shrimp
 Cassava-Stuffed Shrimp, 203
 Chicken and Shrimp Soup, 113
 in Grilled Seafood Salad, 79
 in Seafood and Rice, *224*, 225
 Shrimp Piri Piri, 228, *229*
Side dishes. *See also* Chutneys; Rice dishes; Salads
 Avocado Pap, 89
 Cassava-Avocado Mash, 92
 Cauliflower Fritters, 93
 Corn Mashed Potatoes, 94
 Crispy Avocado, 95
 Fresh Cheese with Chives, 52
 Injera, *144*, 145
 Mango Couscous, 96, *97*
 Pickled Green and Yellow Papayas, 54
 Pickled Onions, 55
 Red Penne, 102
 Shiro, 103
 Shiro-Stuffed Tomatoes, 104
 Spicy Plantain Chips, 106, *107*
Sinbujen, Dakar, Senegal, traveling in, 208–213
Skewered dishes
 Boharat Beef Skewers, 282
 Duck Skewers, 246, *247*
 Lobster Skewers with Couscous-Avocado Salad, 215
 Salmon Skewers with Tamarind Sauce, 223
Snapper
 barbecued, 202
 Snapper Wrapped in Banana Leaves, 230, 231
Sorbet, chocolate-coconut, 313
Soups
 Callaloo, 112
 Caramelized Mango Soup, 314
 Chicken and Shrimp Soup, 113
 Crab Soup, 115
 Grilled Tilapia-Avocado Soup, 122
 Quail–Foie Gras Soup, 125
 Spicy Crayfish Boil, 126
 Squid with Corn-Tomato Soup, 128, *129*
Sources, 336
Sour Tamarind-Almond Balls, 329
South Africa, xxi–xxii, 10, 26, 27, 40, 56, 61, 64, 73, 76, 80, 83, 87, 89, 105, 111, 116–119, 138, 141, 143, 164, 172, 187, 200, 206, 216, 218, 222, 226, 228, 237, 240–241, 268, 273, 274, 276–279, 281, 285, 288, 291, 297, 300–301, 308–312, 322, 324, 333
Spaghetti, trout, 234, *235*
Spice blends and rubs, 9–37
 Awase, 14
 Berbere, 12, *13*
 Black Olive Oil, 15
 Boharat, 17
 Chermoula, 15
 Dark Spice Mix, 18
 Duqqa, 19
 Ginger Paste, 26
 Green Curry Paste, 26
 Green Masala, 27
 Harissa, 30
 Jerk Mix, 31
 Ras Al-Hanout, 32
 Spiced Butter, 34
 Yogurt Rub, 35
 Za'atar, 37
Spiced Bass with Crunchy Rice and Watercress Salad, 232, *233*
Spiced Butter, 34
Spiced Egg Salad, 81
Spice grinder, about, 7
Spice jars, about, 7
Spicy Crayfish Boil, 126
Spicy Okra, 194, *195*
Spicy Plantain Chips, 106, *107*
Spicy Tilapia Stew, 127
Spicy Tuna on Chapatis, 167
Spinach sauce, trout with, 134
Squab, salted, Egyptian-style, 253
Squash
 apple-, fritters, 172
 butternut, eggplant–, salad, warm, 86
Squid with Corn-Tomato Soup, 128, *129*

Steak Tartare, 295
Stews
Chicken Mofongo, 243
Chicken Stew (Doro Wett), *244*, 245
Chicken-Peanut Stew, 114
Cod Stew with Sesame Seeds, 120, *121*
Guinea Hen with Shiro, 255
Lentil Stew, 123
Malata, 216, *217*
Palaver Sauce, 190
Plantain-Coconut Stew, 124
Spicy Tilapia Stew, 127
Stir-Fried Beef Stew, *130*, 131
Trout with Spinach Sauce, 134
Vegetable Tagine, 196
Stir-Fried Beef Stew, *130*, 131
Stir-fry, lamb, 289
Stuffing, 256
Sugar, brown, about, 1
Sukuma wiki, 289
Sumac, about, 5
Sweet potatoes
in Chunky Mashed Vegetables, 176
in Jerk Chicken, 260, 261
Sweet Potato–Coconut Turnovers, 332
Swiss chard, creamed, 177

T

Tagine, about, 7
vegetable, 196
Tamarind, about, 5–6
drink, 334
sauce, salmon skewers with, 223
vinaigrette, 66
Tangerine Consommé with Tapioca, 330, 331
Tapioca, about, 6
tangerine consommé with, 330, 331
Tarragon Mustard, 67
Tartare
steak, 294
Warm Tuna "Tartare", 236
Tea
-roasted veal, 291
iced, mint, 333
Teff, about, 6
Thyme-Roasted Garlic, 68, 69
Tilapia
-avocado, grilled, soup, 122
stew, spicy, 127
Tisane, lemongrass, 334, 335
Toasted Peanut Bread, 153
Toasted Spiced Dried Fruit Bread, 254
Tomato(es)
in Barbecued Oxtail, 272
in Jollof Rice, 265
Lamb-Stuffed Tomatoes, 290
Oysters with Green Tomato Water, 218
sauce, in Falafel with Quick Tomato Sauce, 184, 185
sauce, in Okra Tomato Sauce, 284
sauce, in Tomato Sauce, 71
Shiro-Stuffed Tomatoes, 104
in Spicy Crayfish Boil, 126
in Stir-Fried Beef Stew, *130*, 131
in Squid with Corn-Tomato Soup, 128, *129*
Tomato Date Jam, 70
Tomato-Cucumber Salad, 161
Tomato-Roasted Shark, 237
Toppings
Caramelized Papayas and Plums, 326
Cinnamon Whipped Cream, 316, 317
Traveling in Africa, 10–11, 40–41, 76, 110–111, 138–139, 170–171, 200–201, 240–41, 268–269, 300–301
Addis Ababa, Ethiopia, traveling in, 139, 146–149, 178–181, 248–251
Bahama Spia Farm, Tanzia, 20–25
Dar es Salaam, Tanzania, 82–85
District Six, Cape Town, South Africa, 308–312
J'mal Fna, Marrakech, Morocco, 62–63
Khayelitsha, South Africa, 276–279
Merkata, Addis Ababa, Ethiopia, 178–181
Sinbujen, Dakar, Senegal, 208–213
Wandie's Place, Johannesburg, Africa, 116–119
Trout
Curried Trout with Coconut-Chili Sauce, 207
Trout Spaghetti, 234, 235
Trout with Spinach Sauce, 134
Tsegie (author's biological father), xii
Tuna
in Grilled Seafood Salad with Yogurt Sauce, 79
spicy, on chapatis, 167
as substitute in Seared Cured Yellowtail, 226, 227
"tartare", warm, 236
Turkey
breast, harissa-roasted, 256
legs, dark-spiced, 252
Turnovers, sweet potato–coconut, 332
Tutu, Desmond, ix, 117

U

Ugali, about, 83–84. *See also* Avocado Pap

V

Vanilla bean, about, 6
Veal
ground, in Boerewors Sausage Patties, 281
lamb and, kefta, *160*, 161
shanks, roasted, with apricots and almonds, 294
tea–roasted, 291
Vegetable(s), 169–197. *See also specific types*
Apple-Squash Fritters, 172
Black-Eyed Peas, 173
Candied Yams and Plantains, *174*, 175
Chunky Mashed Vegetables, 176
Creamed Swiss Chard, 177
Crispy Vegetables, 182
Mustard Greens and Corn, 183
Falafel with Quick Tomato Sauce, 184, 185
Palaver Sauce, 190
Pumpkin Mash, 186, 187
Roasted Eggplant and Plantains, 191
Sautéed Morning Glory, 192
Sautéed Vegetables, 193
Spicy Okra, 194, 195

Vegetable Filling, 165
Vegetable Samosas, 165, 166
Vegetable Tagine, 196
Warm Cabbage, 197
Venison loin, duqqa-cured, 297
Vicky's B&B, 277
Vinaigrette, tamarind, 66

Wandie's Place, Johannesburg, Africa, 116–119
Warm Cabbage, 197
Warm Eggplant–Butternut Squash Salad, 86
Warm Potato-Cod Salad, 87
Warm Tuna "Tartare", 236
Watercress, rice and, salad, crunchy, spiced bass with, 232, 233
Wendy (author's friend), 112
West Africa, xix–xx, 10, 41, 44, 45, 67, 84, 92, 94, 101, 111, 112, 114, 115, 140, 153, 159, 171, 173, 175, 190, 200, 201, 202, 203, 205, 208–213, 214, 225, 231, 240, 243, 265, 268, 271, 300, 303, 306, 315, 326, 328, 331
Whipped cream, cinnamon, 316, 317
White Bean Puree, 72
White Bean–Sardine Salad, 88

Yams, about, 6
and plantains, candied, 174, 175
Yellow Rice, 105
Yellowtail
plantain-crusted, 222
seared cured, 226, 227
Yogurt Dip, 73
Yogurt Rub, 35
Yogurt Sauce, 79

Z

Za'atar, 37
Za'atar-Roasted Leg of Lamb, 296
Zalouk. *See* Warm Eggplant–Butternut Squash Salad
Zanzibari "Pizzas", 166